LITTLE
SHIPS
&
SHOAL
WATERS

LITTLE SHIPS & SHOAL WATERS

Designing, Building and Sailing Shoal Draught
Cruising Yachts . . . with a Cruise or
Two in both Blue and Sandy Waters

by Maurice Griffiths

Associate of the Institution of Naval Architects

Author of:
Yachting on a Small Income
The Magic of the Swatchways
Ten Small Yachts and Others
Everyman's Yachting
Dream Ships
The Arrow Book of Sailing
Swatchways and Little Ships
The First of the Tide

CONWAY
MARITIME PRESS

© Maurice Griffiths 1937 and 1985
First published by Peter Davies 1937
Reprinted by Conway Maritime Press 1972
Third impression 1985
Reprinted 1988

ISBN 0 85177 056 8

Conway Maritime Press Ltd.
24 Bride Lane, Fleet Street, London EC4Y 8DR

Printed in Great Britain by R J Acford, Chichester

'With board up she rides like a gull. The seas can't get hold of her.'

Foreword to Third Impression

WHEN this book was first compiled before the outbreak of the Hitler war yachts were still being built with planking and frames, decks and deck beams, knees and floor frames and other parts of the hull of good seasoned timber. Each traditionally-built yacht was therefore composed of hundreds of pieces of wood shaped and fitted carefully together, and fastened with copper rivets or galvanised iron boat nails, bronze or galvanised screws, bolts, iron spikes or metal tie rods.

Dinghies and the smaller cabin boats had lapstrake or clinker planked hulls with steam-bent timbers, while the larger craft were carvel-built with smooth sided hulls, and in many cases substantial frames sawn from good oak to the curves of the hull with two or three steam-bent timbers between each pair of frames. For lightweight hulls various firms had indeed introduced double-skinned planking – diagonal inside, fore and aft outside – in the manner of RNLI lifeboats and naval harbour launches and some speedboats. But the idea of building up hulls with many thin laminations was not yet practicable, for it was to take the war years and the rapid development of the aircraft industry to produce suitable waterproof glues.

The long held dream that many yachtsmen had of doing away with these countless pieces of wood and timber baulks and all the seams subject to rot and leaks of the ordinary yacht hull, and just producing standard hulls from a suitable mix in one piece in a mould like a giant pudding, was yet to come. Even reliable marine plywood for boats was not introduced until the war, when marine glues were to make amateur boat building not only possible, but to start a new do-it-yourself home industry. At the same time the introduction of oil-based resinglass (glass reinforced plastics, or GRP) was to result in an entirely new boat building technique with a phenomenal growth after the war.

Reinforced concrete in the form of a flexible steel mesh basket form, rendered more rigid and completely watertight by a mortar mix, was invented by Professor Luigi Nervi for spring diving boards during the war, and was to have a great vogue in building small ferrocement craft, from Chinese fishing sampans to home products from the backyard, for its technique did not require the skills of the shipwright. All these aspects of boat building, and others like multiple GRP laminations, C-Flex and foam-sandwich, have come into the picture within this war-wracked generation.

This book has set out to describe not only how wooden yachts are constructed, and how an owner sets about having such a little ship built in a yacht yard, but it also aims at showing what advantages the well designed yacht of shoal draught offers not only the family cruising man in coastal waters, but also the ocean cruising crew who enjoy exploring shallow waters and remote rivers and lagoons in other parts of the world. That a shoal draught yacht which may take the ground almost upright, and yet prove a thoroughly able boat in a seaway, has come to be recognised for its admirable qualities for the cruising man can be seen in the thousands of shallow twin bilge keel yachts produced by various firms in recent years.

It can be said that twin bilge keels, with or without a central ballast keel, have superseded the centreboard for coastal cruising and deep sea voyaging. Ranging from the little Robert Tucker designed Silhouette class through the hundreds of *Yachting Monthly* Eventide and Waterwitch bilge keelers to the Golden Hind 31 range with their world-ranging records, there are many other proprietory twin keel cruising yachts in production. These shoal draught bilge keelers form a considerable proportion of family yachts to be found in all parts of the world, all of them able to settle on the ground on occasion in safety and comfort.

In writing this book I owe a debt of gratitude to many friends both in England and in America for the generous assistance they have given me in the research work that has been necessary, and especially do I acknowledge the courtesy of the various designers and owners of the plans, the photographs and much of the material concerning their respective ships that through their kindness I have been able to gather for these pages. Some of these friends, alas, are no longer with us, but to their memory and to those who still love the little ships and the shoal waters I gladly dedicate this book.

West Mersea
Essex 1984   MAURICE GRIFFITHS

Contents

PART ONE

The Art of Planning Shoal Draught Yachts

PART TWO

Some Shoal Draught Cruisers

CONTENTS

PART THREE

Under Way

PART ONE

The Art of Planning
Shoal Draught Yachts

'Acute Discomfort'

While *Tewk*, a typical 6-ton keel cutter, lies at this angle on the sands, a shoal draught centreboarder would be appreciably more comfortable.

I

But—Why Shoal Draught?

'Hope springs eternal in the human breast'

M ANY yachtsmen, fatalists in other walks of life and perhaps hard-headed in business matters, spend the greater part of their lives dreaming of an Ideal Cruiser. Men are incurably romantic where ships and the sea—and certain other subjects—are concerned, and the quest for the dream-ship, a cruising boat which will have all the virtues and none of the vices inseparable from all existing craft, is a pursuit that occupies the waking thoughts—aye, and the dreams too—of many a man with salt in his veins.

It is undoubtedly one of the eternal charms of yacht cruising, or of that never-ending source of pleasure to sailing men—just 'talking boats', that there can be no such phenomenon as an ideal cruiser; and when a man steps back and looks at the question sensibly with a view perspective, he will have to acknowledge, if he is honest with himself, that such a thing is impossible. In this mortal world, with its many intricacies of cause and effect, its infinite varieties of good and bad, just and evil, its natural laws and primitive logic, it is impossible for Man to make something so intricate as a boat, so enthralling as a ship, which shall be perfect and a delight in every particular. There will always be something wrong. Every action has its reaction and every desirable thing has its snags. Yet so alluring is the feeling that the dream-ship will be perfect where all others fail, that no amount of discouragement will deter many yachtsmen from dreaming and planning a small ship that 'one day' they say 'will carry me through the Bay and before the Trades to—freedom'.

I should not like to think that I have become an incurable cynic or a pessimist beyond the power of prayer, but in a busy stretch of sixteen years, four of them taken up as a yacht broker and yachting writer and the remaining twelve as an editor, author and yacht designer, I have met a very large number of sailing men, have read many hundreds of stories and articles and letters from others, and have learned a fair amount about this way of life called yacht cruising, and it seems to me that the idea of sailing solemnly alone or with one companion across the world in a small yacht as one's final goal in life, with perhaps the isles of the Pacific as the haven where all will end well, is about as sensible as a desire to nose a pea to the top of a mountain—an art at present, I believe, exclusively American. Although, like the majority of people who are bitten by the cruising bug, I began by imagining that my ultimate joy would be a sound, tight little ship in which I could cruise the world to my heart's content, finding perfect happiness in a life of untrammelled freedom, I no longer try to kid myself in this way. I know that I should just hate to be boxed up in a small, restless boat week after week, blow high or blow calm, with naught to do but loaf into various harbours of the world, searching for—what?

Happiness? Who but a fool sails across oceans in quest of happiness? It comes from within us, like hope and despair and anger and love. One does not find it alone in a small yacht in

3

the Pacific or the Azores or the isles of the East. An occasional ocean passage from the Pacific Coast to Honolulu or from Falmouth to the West Indies, in a well-found sea-kindly little vessel, with several congenial and competent companions, is in a different category. Like a good story it has a reasoned beginning, a sense of adventure, good companionship, a definite aim and an ending that together make it a complete experience most of us hope to enjoy one of these days.

But the itinerant tramp, like a hobo' of the seas, who sets out alone or with an equally doubtful partner to beg his way across the seas is no credit to the sport of sailing or the name of cruising. Many men, it is true, do fit out little ships and spend months wandering around the world, with apparently no other end in view, but I have never met one yet who did not strike me as being an oddity amongst his fellow creatures. But for every man who is content to continue this strange and inhuman way of life a score of others set forth for their Eldorado and come back disillusioned, generally much wiser and invariably broke. And they hardly ever bring back their dream-ships with them.

The yarns that are printed describing these long voyages make good reading. I suppose I have read most of those published and a large number that have never appeared in print ; an occasional dip into one or other of the classics—Slocum, Robinson, Gerbault, O'Brien, Stock and Voss—is always a pleasure, and I am well acquainted with the disturbing effect such books can have on men who are bored with their daily living or discontented with their lot on shore. The very sight of a harbour of shipping with its unchanging smells fires the imagination ; for there is indeed something about the smell of a ship that stirs a man's blood, a seductive, persuasive odour of oak and tarred rope and canvas and paint, of varnish and oil and galley smoke and rust, that exciting scent that clings like an aura to every shapely little schooner with her jib-boom steeved above the quays, and drifts on the breeze from every fishing smack that puts to sea ; a haunting smell that goes to a man's head like wine and makes him yearn for a free life, open air and a wide horizon, and above all for the kick of a tiller under his arm and the scend of a stout little ship beneath his feet. . . .

Oh, I know. When a man ceases to want to run away to sea he can be sure that he has finally left youth behind him. Many men indeed never fully become adults ; they are ever ready to be excited by the chance that life at sea or in any other part of the world will be different and much more enjoyable. It is always good to have that hope in moderation.

But by far the majority of yachtsmen are either compelled by the ties of home and jobs, or are just content to limit their cruising accomplishments to coastal sailing and pottering about the inlets of our own shores. Whatever dreams they may have of

' Wide horizons and a Trade Wind snoring '

in practice their ideas of an enjoyable cruise are confined within the limits of their own way of cruising, the week-end sailing of the average business yachtsman.

Because at least nine-tenths of their sailing is done within sight of the land and their anchorages are places where there is little room to swing and none too' much water, they do not really need a yacht which has been designed solely for deep sea, long distance cruising. It seems to me lacking in a sense of proportion to buy a big and heavy, deep draught boat whose every item of gear and equipment, above decks and below, has been planned for blue water cruising,

4

Windflower has a long leading edge despite her shoal draught

WINDFLOWER, 21 Tons

WHAT can be done on a limited draught is shown by these photographs of a very handsome 45-ft. keel yawl which was built at Emsworth, Hampshire, in 1928. Designed by E. P. Hart, *Windflower* has the long forefoot with the slight knuckle in the profile at the forward end of the keel associated with this designer (cf. *Har Jeff*) and although this ship is 33 ft. WL and 12·2-ft. beam, her draught is only 5 ft. Rigged as a gaff yawl, her working sail area is 1,055 sq. ft. Unfortunately her plans were destroyed some years ago in a fire and cannot be reproduced here.

Although to eyes accustomed to deep yachts her underwater body may appear inadequate for windward work and deep sea cruising, she has proved herself a fine, able craft, and her former owner, Colonel Buckle, writes :

' In seven years of cruising I found *Windflower* absolutely perfect on every point of sailing. She stood up to her canvas extremely well and sailed at a moderate angle of heel. She is a good sea boat,

Firm bilges make up for a shallow keel

dry and buoyant and carries her way well through the short seas on the East Coast. In my opinion she is a magnificent example of what we East Coast men know full well, our smacks are fine boats on about 4 ft. 6 in. draught. *Windflower* exemplifies very well the argument one frequently sees in print, that a good designer can produce a light draught hull much more suitable for yachting. If I am ever to have another ship, I could think of nothing better than to go to Hart and ask him to design another *Windflower*. Her draught is not an inch over 5 ft. at the deepest, but she was designed so that her inside lead could be added to the keel making the draught 6 ft. if it was found she wanted it. She certainly doesn't want it for cruising purposes and although I had it in mind to make the alteration, I became convinced that I should lose more than I gained by so doing. What always struck me as the really clever part of *Windflower's* design, apart from her beautiful lines, was that without any excessive freeboard she had 6 ft. 2 in. of headroom everywhere and gave the impression inside of a deep ship.'

5

if all you need her for in reality—as apart from dreams—is for week-end estuary pottering and limited coastal cruising. Flush decked, deep draught craft having stuffy ill-lighted cabins like deep wells, and shallow exposed self-draining cockpits, may be very safe and fine healthy sea boats a thousand miles from land, but handling such a boat in the usual crowded home anchorages and getting her under way for a short passage around the coast brings out all her bad qualities and inconvenience and tends to make week-end cruising very hard work.

It is far more reasonable for the week-end yachtsman who has to be back in his office on Monday morning to have a boat specially planned for *his* way of cruising without this absurd pretence that, although he uses her now only for short cruises, he will need her sooner or later for sailing around the world. Many men enjoy pretending that and have quite unsuitable boats solely to give realism to the pretence. But they will not admit it.

In order to reap the greatest satisfaction from estuary cruising and the most pleasure from unashamed creek exploring it is essential to have the right type of boat, and this means not only a handy and fast little ship, but also a boat that will take the mud, whether by design or accident, at a safe angle of heel and not be in the slightest danger of filling on the next tide. This means, of course, some sort of shallow draught ship.

In Great Britain, in addition to the Thames estuary there are numerous places where shallow draught is a great advantage, and owners of such craft are glad of their particular qualities at many ports such as Chichester, Christchurch and Poole Harbours near the Wight, in Morecambe Bay and the estuary of the Dee, on the Humber and the Yorkshire rivers and even around the sandy anchorages of the Mersey. In the West Country, on that lovely Devon and Cornish coast, almost the home of the deep keeled cruising and work boat, the shoal draught yacht still has advantages, for many of the most charming harbours dry out at low water, and the rivers with their miles of sand banks and tortuous channels are accessible only to boats with flat bilges. Exploring the Exe with its miles of sand banks, the Dart to Totnes, the Tamar and the Lynher rivers far into Devon, even the lovely upper creeks of Falmouth Harbour, is more an anxiety than a simple pleasure in a boat whose deep keel and sharp bottom make a few hours on a sandbank a period of purgatory ; and it may be remembered that Sir Harold Clayton, whose home is in the West, built for himself a fine centreboard cruising yawl, the 30 ton *Zinita*, as long ago as 1910, which was designed almost solely to enable her to lie in these shallow West Country harbours and the smaller estuaries without that risk of falling over on legs that is ever present with a deep boat.

Yachtsmen who like to have ' plenty of boat under them ' are given to think that the shoal draught cruiser is suitable only for sheltered waters and is much too unsafe to take to sea. Old prejudices die hard and the Anglo-Saxon ones hardest of all, for although this theory has been disproved time and again, it can be truthfully said that the *average* yachtsman on both sides of the Atlantic believes that in order to have a good sea boat one must have a deep keel and, of course, the resulting heavy displacement. In defence of this theory there is always some reference to ' clawing off a lee shore ' as though you only needed a boat with deep draught to be able to do that : whereas very few yachts indeed under 40 ft. LWL in all probability would be able to claw off a lee shore against a *full* gale of wind, whether they drew three feet or ten.

6

I am not concerned here with miraculous ability to thresh to windward through white broken water in the very jaws of death. The circumnavigator of the globe may conceivably land himself and his ship in such a predicament in some cruel bay at the other end of the world, but I assume that my readers are normal boat owners whose cruising is limited in the main to Long Island Sound, the Atlantic coast line, or the narrow seas of Great Britain. Such conditions, therefore, as a dangerous lee shore and being hopelessly embayed are not likely to be encountered ; so unlikely are they, indeed, for the average business-yachtsman who does not spend his life at sea that I do not see the need to put up with an inconvenient boat merely because she *might*, if put to it, be able to claw off a lee shore in a gale.

That boats of shoal draught are not necessarily bad sea boats has been demonstrated in every part of the world over a period of centuries, and even in the British Isles no better proof of the ability of light draught craft in extreme conditions of wind and sea could be given than the record of the Royal National Lifeboat Institution around the stormy coasts of Britain. No one, I believe, has yet suggested that lifeboats—even those that lie afloat on their own moorings —would be better and safer seaboats if they had deep keels.

For his famous voyage around the world Captain Slocum had in *Spray* a boat with 13 ft. 10 in. beam and but 4 ft. draught, without any centreboard. According to Slocum's account of his cruise there was never the slightest doubt of the boat's ability to ride out any gale she encountered, while her almost phenomenal accomplishment of steering herself indefinitely when running would not, I am inclined to believe, have been possible if her keel had been deepened and, say, her garboards given a sharper rise.

Other transoceanic voyagers have clung to boats of very light draught through no necessity but solely from choice, amongst them old Thomas Drake who built four different little ships and sailed each one some of the way across the world. They were all, I believe, chine or deadrise boats and all double ended. *Pilgrim*, which he built without help at Seattle and sailed through the Panama Canal and across the Atlantic only to wreck her on the Dutch shoals, had about 12 ft. beam but drew only 3 ft. 6 in. I boarded her while she lay off Westminster Pier and she then gave me the impression, rough and crude as she was, of obvious sterling seagoing qualities and of being as safe as a steamship at sea. The two earlier boats which Drake built had also been similar with but 3½ ft. draught and the last one, *Progress*, a development of *Pilgrim*, is again of the flat V-sectioned shoal draught type.

If we look farther afield, searching for small vessels that put to sea for long periods, we find that the seagoing Chinese junk, which for centuries has made long voyages out into the Pacific and across the Timor Sea and the Indian Ocean, has an extremely flat and shallow hull. In place of leeboards or a centreboard there is a deep, narrow rudder, perforated with many holes to ease the pressure on it without affecting the efficiency of its ' leading edge ', which acts in the same way as a simple dagger plate in a dinghy. With sails on deck and, if necessary, masts lowered, the seagoing junk rides out heavy weather that would give a deeper and heavier vessel a terrible punishing.

In the Pacific itself we find records of almost unbelievably long voyages made by the Polynesians in their big canoes, and they had no more need of deep keels and heavy displacement than the lifeboats of the *Trevessa* or the *Bounty's* boat in which Bligh made his historic voyage.

In his book *The Yacht 'Alice'* my old friend Henry Howard states the case for the centre-boarder at sea in lucid terms. With the *Alice*, a ketch 52 ft. OA, 44 ft. WL, 13·6 ft. beam and only 4 ft. draught with the wooden centreboard up, Mr. Howard and his family have cruised up and down the east coast of Florida and in the Bahamas and West Indies for several winters. *Alice* was not an experiment : her hull form was the result of the fifty years of experience in designing shoal draught seagoing yachts of Commodore Munroe, an eminent American designer. She has lain hove-to in heavy winds more than once, and one of the crew, describing a bad weather passage he had made with the Howards, told me ' With the board up the *Alice* lay hove-to under double reefed main only. Below in one's bunk you couldn't hear a sound, and the motion seemed so gentle that at first I thought the gale had blown itself out. But when I poked my head through the main hatch, why I nearly had my teeth blown in ! The ship was lifting and falling gently over the big Atlantic rollers, sidling down their faces and leaving a kinda slick to windward, and the crested seas just couldn't get hold of her. If she had been a deep keel boat and set herself solidly in the water, she'd have had to stand a deal of heavy punishment in that blow.'

The historic case of the loss with all hands of the heavy, deep keel 100 ft. English yawl *Cythera* off Sandy Hook in the famous March blizzard of 1888, when but a few miles away the 63 ft. Yankee centreboard schooner *Whim* rode it out under bare poles and with her board hauled up, with no heavy water on deck and without sustaining any damage, has been called upon more than once to show how the very depth of keel and the enormous grip of the water of a deep draught craft can prove her undoing. In this case the ill-fated *Cythera* drew 13 ft. while *Whim*, with board raised, drew but 3 ft. 3 in.

When the breaking sea hits a deep keeler hove-to there is no ' give ' in her : she resists the pressure of the water to push her bodily to leeward, and instead of the blow being softened the crest hits her full and hearty and perhaps sweeps her decks clear. Lifeboat men know this from experience under extreme conditions of wind and sea, and whoever heard of a deep keel, heavy displacement lifeboat ? And in defence of this Mr. Henry Howard quotes the old pilots of Southport, North Carolina, who used to sail 100 miles or more into the Atlantic blow high blow low : ' There is no argument as far as we are concerned ', they told him when discussing deep versus light draught boats, ' because we know from years of experience that the light draught craft is far more comfortable and safer in riding out bad weather off shore.'

Some years ago I was hove-to under staysail only in a Falmouth quay punt during a sudden and quite heavy blow near the West Hinder L. V. (Force 9 was recorded for this area when later I applied to the Meteorological Office.) Although the yacht had no appreciable forward way she was hit time after time by those angry combers that make this part of the North Sea such a bad place. The crashes against the obstinate weather bow were frightening to hear, but the ship, deep in the water and her decks constantly filled, stood against the onslaught until as the hours went by I began to fear she would open up her seams. Miserably sick and anxious for the boat as I was, it was an unpleasant but enlightening experience.·

Some time later I hove-to in a shallow draught cutter in fairly similar conditions. The wind was not quite at gale strength—perhaps force 6—and with this game little ship there was no actual necessity to heave-to, but I wanted to watch her behaviour. Unlike the deep keeler she did not stand still and let the breaking seas batter her, her lee drift left a smooth or 'slick' for three or four yards to windward which seemed to smooth down the crests, while when a sea did break it generally tumbled over before it reached her, as though the hull managed to sidle away and avoid all the promised punishment.

I have always thought that W. E. Sinclair's game little 4-tonner *Joan* was knocked flat, dismasted and finally abandoned in the North Atlantic chiefly because she had such an immense grip of the water. She was of the Falmouth quay punt type and although only some 22 ft. overall she drew 5 ft. 6 in. with a very deep forefoot, and it seems to me likely that when hove-to she sat almost immovably in the water and let the seas hit her as though she were a half tide rock. No one, however, saw the sea that did overwhelm her—it might have been such that any boat would have been rolled over by it—and my theory is advanced here only as a theory and not as the slightest aspersion on seamanship or quay punts in general. Nor must it be thought that I am trying to prove the theories of the man who feels he is safe only when he has plenty of boat beneath him to be 'all wrong.' Quite the majority of British yachtsmen believe in the theory of deep boats for seaworthiness and, except in the most extreme conditions, I am sure they *are* quite *safe* : but it does not mean that the centreboard yacht need not be every bit as seaworthy and safe.

The 40-year-old schooner *Brown, Smith and Jones*, owned by George P. Brett, Jr.,
is a true bugeye from Chesapeake Bay.

II

Centreboards and Centreplates

UNTIL a few years ago yacht architecture as a profession in Great Britain was more conservative and hidebound than any other—with the possible exception of the medical profession—
and it was not until one or two young designers with progressive ideas put their theories into
practice and gave us some fine ocean going small yachts that the general apathy surrounding
the entire cult of designing and cruising yachts was stirred.

It is not an exaggeration to say, indeed, that the development of the modern fast cruising
yacht along what can largely be described as ocean racing lines, in place of the heavy displacement tubs of pre-war days, owes much of its success to the concerted work of the young Olin
Stephens and one or two others in America, and of Uffa Fox and Laurent Giles in England,
with the widespread assistance given by the yachting press of both continents. What had been
only hinted in Colin Archer's designs, and in those graceful little ships of the late G. U. Laws,
Dixon Kemp and Albert Strange, had passed over the heads of those of us who came after,
groping with our splines and our T-squares for the best type of cruising yacht; and it has been
left to progressive young naval architects on both sides of the Atlantic to show why our old-
time theories are wrong and why better yachts could be designed than had ever left the quays,
if only one were bold and could break away from the accepted conventions. Thus *Dorade*,
Edlu, *Stormy Weather*, *Vamarie*, *Kirawan*, *Trenchemer*, *Foxhound*, *Bloodhound*, *If*, *Latifa* and others
of the beautiful, slim form came to be born, and a distinct new era in the design of fast cruisers
has begun.

Coincident with this almost sudden development came the searching theories on the
balance of sailing yacht hulls advanced by Engineer Rear Admiral Alfred Turner, whose consistent letters on a fascinating subject in the *Yachting Monthly* gave rise to the ' Metacentric
Shelf ' method of hull design. A full explanation of this form of design analysis was written for
the *Yachting Monthly* by Dr. Harrison Butler and published in the January and February
numbers, 1937.

Briefly, this system takes into consideration the position of the metacentre at each one of the sections or stations on the plan when the hull is heeled to a normal sailing angle, usually taken as 20°, in a whole sail breeze. These positions when plotted form a curve of a curious twisted shape, and it is the shape of this curve that will tell the man who understands it whether the design under test will in theory balance perfectly at all angles of heel (that is, will carry the same slight weather helm in light breezes or heavy, and with the wind on the bow, beam or quarter) or will reveal latent vices when pressed. The famous case of the ex-Kaiser's *Meteor* which, when pressed to her beam ends by a squall, took charge, paid off and roared away to leeward with all the sheets belayed under four feet of water, is a perfect example of a yacht whose meta-centric shelf would—or should—reveal such a possible trait in time for the designer to correct it.

From some of the yachts which have been designed under the metacentric shelf test, such as *Fidelis* and *Mystery*, it is certain that a perfectly balanced hull can be proved when checked by this method : but while awed by the sweeping enthusiasms of the metacentricists the query has always persisted in my own mind whether such a hull must necessarily be fast, or possess excellent windward qualities, say, in a short sea, or behave as an ideal *cruiser* should under all of the many varying conditions that a small cruising yacht may have to face ; and so far as I know this has not yet been proved. Maybe I am a sceptic on ' systems ' of all kinds, but one must admit that there have been many different systems introduced for producing the true form of hulls for sailing vessels ever since shipwrights began to work with a pair of compasses, and each system of ship design has had its breathless followers. Yet, you know, not one of them has succeeded in producing the ideal yacht or the perfect hull.

Admiral Turner's mathematical check on designs has been wholeheartedly embraced by more than one designer and no doubt the resultant boats are an improvement on his previous efforts, but I feel inclined to look at the matter bye and large and to wait for some proof that a small cruiser at least is not better, say at windward work, if she carries a fair amount of weather helm and has in her lines that extra fullness or buoyancy or power (call it what you will) that would not conform to the metacentric shelf theory of perfect balance. While perfect balance on the helm may be desirable in a racing yacht with a short keel and comparatively long over-hangs and a continual joy to the helmsman in the type of craft which conforms to the require-ments of the metacentric shelf test, I am certain that it is not conducive to a good all round shoal draught cruiser.

Unfortunately British professional yacht designers as a rule know little about the peculiar problems and the essential features of the good shallow draught sailing cruiser. The trouble is that with yachtsmen in this country suffering from the naval architectural sins of their grand-fathers, they have avoided the use of centreboards as being something that the Yankees did to boats and too much akin to a ' contrivance ', and the yacht designing profession in England has therefore omitted shoal draught and centreboards from its regular curriculum as the medical profession has eschewed birth control and mental phobias as normal medical studies.

This may appear to be an unnecessarily sweeping statement—if not rank heresy—but if one asks just how many really good and successful centreboard cruising yachts have been built in Great Britain to *professional* designs, the answer is illuminating : one has to look long and searchingly to find more than half a dozen well planned centreboard cruisers which are not the studied work of an amateur.

When I first began to study the design of shoal draught seagoing cruising yachts a decade or so back, I discovered that there was scarcely any literature at all on the subject in England, that no one, with the exception of a knowledgeable amateur here and there, knew anything about it, and as for existing good examples of this type of craft there did not appear to be any in British waters. I soon found that one had to turn to the United States, admittedly the home of the centreboard, for information and advice on the theory of shoal draught and light displacement and for the study of boats of this type.

Not all American designers, of course, design centreboard boats, but I think the majority of them know how to. It is many years since the great battles were fought up and down the Atlantic seaboard between apoplectic gentlemen called cuttercranks by their opponents and equally excited gentlemen wedded to centreboards. This controversy assumed in yacht racing circles almost the importance of the Civil War, which was still fresh in the minds of some of the opponents, who took it with the same seriousness. Neither side, needless to say, was convinced by the other's arguments or proofs ; rather each was comfortably strengthened in its own convictions, the British side particularly with its ideas of ' plenty of boat beneath you for safety and comfort at sea.'

Those who just *prefer* deep keeled boats and feel happy to know there is a deep and heavy hull beneath them with a slow scending motion and an ability to lie-to almost dead still when they put to sea, continued to have such boats built, while the others who like nosing into the numerous little shallow sounds and harbours of the eastern seaboard and do not object to the quicker movements at sea of a centreboard boat, continued to enjoy their way of cruising in their favourite type of boat and to pour scorn on the advocates of any other type. I am convinced that in no sport is so much contempt felt for the other man's ideas as in yachting.

The American yachtsman has a national advantage where shallow draught boats are concerned. He has grown up accustomed to seeing centreboard boats, for not only are most of the fishing craft and oyster boats on the eastern seaboard of this type, but a number of coastal schooners have always been fitted with centreboards. There are such large expanses of shoal water and so many shallow bays, harbours and inlets in Delaware Bay, Chesapeake Bay, Pamlico Sound, Long Island Sound, the 'inland passages' south to the Carolina Sounds and, for those with larger boats to face the Atlantic, the unlimited shallow water cruising grounds of the Bahamas, that centreboard craft have had every inducement to develop in the United States. And their development has not been tardy.

Just as in England many cutter yachts have copied the local smacks, shrimpers and bawleys in design and rig, so many small yachts in America have followed the traditional lines of the local work boats : and there are many yachts which are developments of the Cape Cod cat-boats, the New Haven sharpies, the Hamptom flatties, the Chesapeake skipjacks and the shallow bugeye schooners. Without the prejudice against shoal draught that persists in England and with the demand for cruising boats which shall not be excluded from these attractive sounds and inlets, it is not surprising that American yacht architects have brought the design of such craft to a higher state of development at any rate than the British.

In England yachtsmen are at last slowly becoming more aware of the possibilities as well as the great advantage of the shallow draught cruiser, and now that the properly designed motor

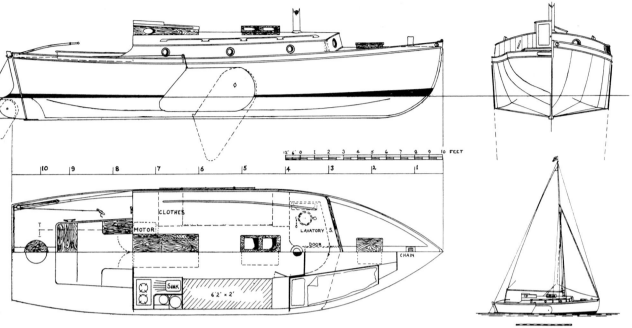

MOORHEN

Design for a small English-type barge yacht by the author. LOA 30 ft., Beam 8 ft. 6 in., Draught 1 ft. 6 in. and 4 ft. 3 in. with iron leeboards down. Headroom under coachroof beams—which extend to the rail each side—is 4 ft. 10 in. and 5 ft. 3 in. under main hatch.

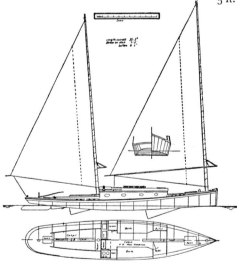

Yachts built on the lines of the New Haven (Conn.) sharpies are very characteristic, usually with two centreboards, two jib headed sails each with revolving masts for reefing and no stays, and a balanced rudder. The bottom is quite flat even at the bow, which causes bad pounding at anchor. This drawing of a 35-ft. by 7.2-ft. sharpie is from Howard I. Chapelle's *American Sailing Craft*.

sailer—not, be it noted, the only half-sail-half-motor 'fifty-fifty'—is slowly coming into its own and appealing to both the time limited motor cruising men and the free sailing men, I foresee that a very large number of shallow cruising yachts will be built in the future. And when more British designers begin to learn that the centreboard installation has to meet several essential requirements if it is not to be a continual source of trouble to the owner, then the centreboard will no longer be regarded as an invention of the Devil—or worse still, of those darned Yankees.

If the collection of designs brought together in this book, together with my own humble notes and observations, has the effect of improving the breed of shoal draught cruising yachts in general, I can ask for no greater satisfaction from a pleasant labour.

In studying all the designs of such craft that I could unearth, by American and British as well as Continental naval architects, I must admit that one or two of the British professionally designed centre-

13

Two Local American Types

This design by John G. Aden, naval architect of Boston, Mass., shows a typical Cape Cod catboat. The high, almost straight stem, the bold sheer, the broad flat transom stern, the 'barn door' rudder, the big wooden centreboard, the great beam and the single mainsail with the mast stepped close to the stem are features of the true 'cat'. This one measures 28 ft. overall, 12 ft. 6 in. beam and 3 ft. 2 in. draught (ex-C.B.).

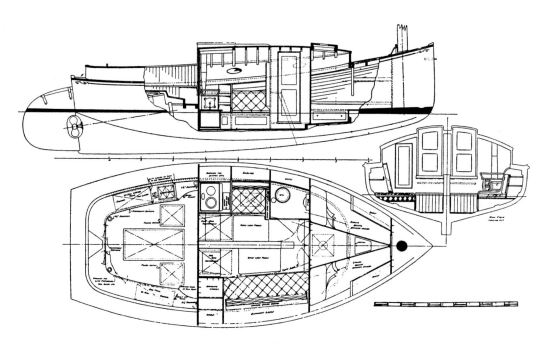

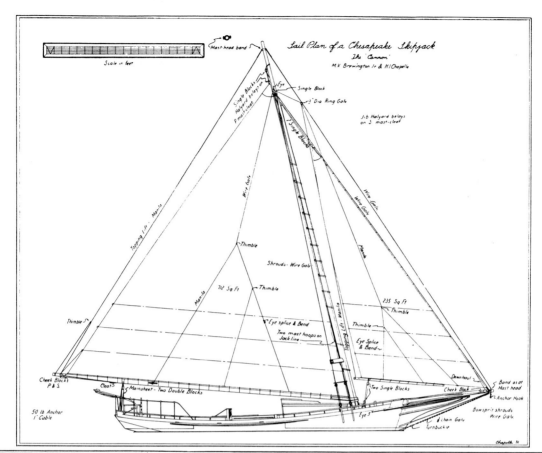

Sail Plan of a Chesapeake Skipjack
The "Cannon"
M.V. Brewington Jr & H I Chapelle

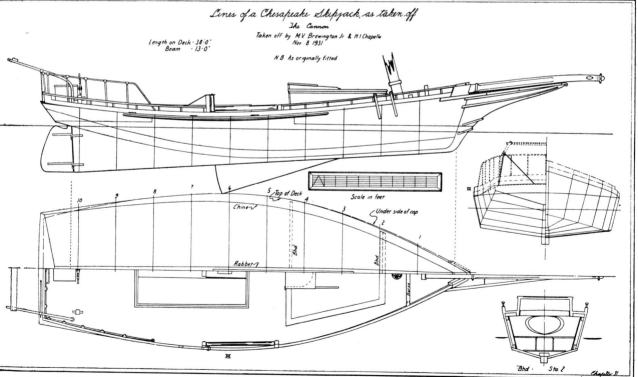

Lines of a Chesapeake Skipjack, as taken off
The Cannon
Taken off by M V Brewington Jr & H I Chapelle
Nov 8 1931

N B As originally fitted

Length on Deck · 38·0
Beam · 13·0

Scale in feet

lans of a typical Chesapeake Bay skipjack, 38 ft. by 13 ft. beam, kindly supplied by Mr. H. I. Chapelle. These plans were taken off the
kipjack *The Cannon* in 1931, and show a type of commercial vessel much used in the shoal waters of the Virginian and Maryland sounds.

board yachts appeared to have all the vices possible with this contrivance. One imagines the designer saying to himself : ' Oh, so this fellow wants a beastly centreboard, does he ? Well now, if I give him a decent draught he'll probably never use it, and you must be able to get to windward. We'll put it, say, here, pivot it there and build a nice teak case on it. Get it right out of sight, that's the idea. Aha, the table perhaps can be hinged on it. Simplicity is the watchword, my boy, just a triangular plate and a neat little winch for raising it at the after end of the table. Well, there it is, if he *must* have a centreboard.'

And I can imagine what the unhappy owner has had to say later on when the plate has strained his case so that it leaks continuously, or when the wire pendant has broken and the plate, hanging downwards on its forward bolt, has become nicely bent and refuses to return into its slot. Probably he has exclaimed ' Curse these devilish contrivances ! ' whereas, if he knew it, he should have said ' Confound that stupid designer ! '

Bad centreboards can certainly be possessed of more vices than one would imagine possible with a contrivance which appears so simple, but this is largely due to the fact that centreboards in the past have usually been built into yachts by boat builders who have no ideas on the subject and have probably themselves never sailed centreboard yachts.

Just as an incompetent builder will almost ruin the reputation of a good make of marine engine by installing it badly and causing the owner endless trouble, so the faulty installation of a centreboard can damn the whole contrivance in the eyes of yachtsmen. Let us, then, consider the essentials which every centreboard should satisfy. There are six, namely :

(1) The case should be so made and installed as not to leak under ordinary conditions.

(2) The centreboard should not be able to drop right down if the pendant breaks.

(3) It should be possible to examine and replace the chain or wire pendant while the yacht is afloat or under way.

(4) The plate or board should be easy to lift out for repair.

(5) When right down in the sailing position there should be ample area of the plate or board left in the keel slot to take the wringing strains imposed upon it under the worst conditions.

(6) The plate or board should never be too heavy to handle with the winch or tackle available.

The material to be used for the centreplate or board depends on the size of the yacht and her nationality. In England galvanized iron or mild steel plate is most common, although in very small boats bronze or brass centreboards are sometimes known, and in two cases that I have come across thick lead sheet has been used. The last, of course, was always liable to be badly buckled and is certainly not to be recommended in any circumstances.

In the British Dominions and United States the majority of C.B. yachts, especially vessels of 30 ft. WL and over, have centreboards built up of one or more layers of wood suitably weighted to enable them to lower of their own accord. The built-up wooden board has many advantages over an iron plate, the lack of excessive weight, freedom from bending and ease of handling being the chief. Indeed, those who have had much experience of centreboard craft, whether yachts or commercial vessels, agree that, except for very small boats, the wooden centreboard is vastly better in almost every way than the heavy iron or steel plate.

There is no advantage in a very heavy centreplate, the added stability of such a plate when right down being more than counterbalanced by its *heeling* tendency in a squall by the pressure of the water on its lee side. Indeed, in some light draught boats and dinghies, when they have little way on and are to be hit by a squall it is sometimes safer to haul up the centreplate so as to allow the squall to push the boat broadside to leeward until she has gathered way and got under control of the helm.

Of the main types of centreboards in use, Fig. 1 shows the most usual, being simply a rectangular plate or laminated board pivoted either through the case or the keel at the forward end and raised by a wire or chain pendant shackled to the after end.

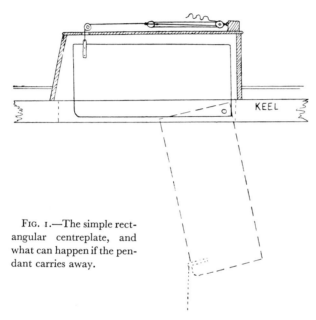

FIG. 1.—The simple rectangular centreplate, and what can happen if the pendant carries away.

If left in the hands of an ordinary builder no form of stop is usually fitted to take the weight of the plate off the lifting tackle when lowered, or, more important still, to prevent the plate from dropping right down as shown in dotted lines, and buckling from the excessive side pressure as soon as the lifting tackle, wire or chain breaks or the shackle pin works out. (Any of which is always liable to happen however easy it may be to lift off the case top for inspection. It just happens like that in this mortal world.) A stop bolt is easily fitted and may prevent untold trouble, especially if the pivot bolt is through the keel and not through the case inside the boat, and so cannot be withdrawn to allow the bent plate to fall clear of the ship before she grounds.

Fig. 2 shows a different type of plate frequently to be found in boat builders' yachts. It is a very unsatisfactory pattern. Possibly this looks neater than the rectangular type, it will take up less space in the cabin and it will also weigh considerably less. But the damaging feature is that when down it leaves so little of the plate in the keel slot that it is almost bound to buckle when the yacht is carried to leeward by a heavy beam sea, or hits the ground when sailing hard, and once this happens (Fig. 2B) the plate cannot be hauled back again. The boat is

17

then compelled to go up on a slip with the centreboard still down, unless the plate can be let go from the pivoted end, and in all probability she will have strained herself and will be leaking badly.

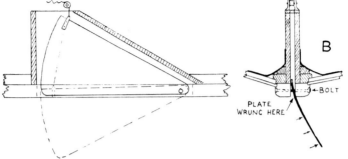

Fig. 2.—The triangular plate, and how it can buckle under heavy strain.

Fig. 3 shows the 'L' type centreboard introduced, I believe, by Albert Strange, who fitted it to a number of his Humber yawls. This type, with the extension piece coming through a slot in the deck which was generally between the mast and the cabin top, or above the top of the extended case, is virtually trouble free and, having the fore and aft case enclosed, this lug can

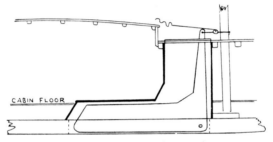

Fig. 3.—The 'L' type of centreplate.

be worked into the accommodation as desired. In my opinion it is a good type of centreboard, but because of its narrow shape it generally has to be of iron or steel. I used this for two of my early centreboard designs—*Wind Song*, 7 tons and *Loon*, 9 tons. In both cases the mast was stepped at the *after* end of the lug case in a tabernacle which formed a very rigid partner to

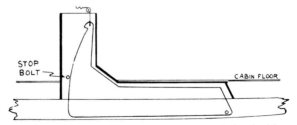

Fig. 4.—Another 'L' type with pendant at after end, fitted with stop bolt.

hold the case, while the lower part of the case was almost entirely below the cabin floor. This type of board is very easily lifted out through the deck slot for repairs, while it cannot drop right down, and should it ever become jammed it can be levered up or down from the deck.

CENTREBOARDS AND CENTREPLATES

In Fig. 4 an equally good type of centreplate or board is shown which again can conform with all six essentials. A stop bolt for preventing the plate from dropping right down in case of breakage of the pendant can be arranged by means of a slight projection on the lug of the plate which rests on the stop bolt when lowered. This is a type which appears to have been adopted most frequently by designers in recent years in the United States, and in one or two good amateur designs in this country.

Many ingenious shapes of centreboards have been introduced in American yacht designs to enable the designer to use the case as a fore and aft bulkhead or a table support or for some other purpose. If, for example, the type in Fig. 3 brought the upright case at the wrong end of the saloon, and the one in Fig. 4 had it too far aft, then a compromise may be worked in as in Fig. 5 with the upright part of the case in the middle. In this example the only part of the centreboard case which rises above the cabin sole (or floor) is cleverly used as a support for the table, and except for the windlass for the hoisting gear (which again could be placed almost anywhere else convenient) one need hardly know there was a centreboard in the ship. The slot-and-bolt form of drop stop shown in Fig. 5 is neat and, if it is desired to save weight,

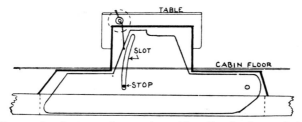

FIG. 5.—Another type of centreplate with radius slot for stop bolt.

could, of course, be used in the Fig. 4 type of plate equally well in place of the lug projection.

I have stressed the danger of the centreboard dropping right down if the pendant breaks. My experience is that however easy it is to examine the wire pendant, there will surely come a time when, quite unexpectedly no doubt, the wire will break, a link of the chain go, or the shackle pin come out. Most centreboards damage themselves so badly and become buckled beyond repair if they do drop right down when the boat is sailing, that it is a contingency to be guarded against. I should personally rather be sure that it cannot happen than rely on keeping the chain or the wire and its shackles in perfect order. It is asking too much of human nature to look after it all as carefully as that. Yachtsmen never do.

Generally in ships as in life the simplest things are best in the long run, and ingenuity in the design of the centreplate does not necessarily spell success. The examples of iron centreplates illustrated, ingenious in their way, however, do not equal in effectiveness and ease of handling an ordinary, plain, rectangular wooden centreboard with a simple lifting tackle and a simple stop bolt in case of trouble.

Apart from the working of the centreboard and its general design, the manner in which it is installed by the builder is of vital importance for its success. I should not like to say how many centreboards I have inspected which have constantly leaked and given other troubles from the day the unfortunate boat was launched. It must be remembered that owing to the immense

19

lateral pressure on a plate that is exposing perhaps, we will say, 15 sq. ft. of surface to the water, the wringing strain inside the case is tremendous. If you imagine what happens when beating to windward against a steep sea, when the yacht lifts up the face of a wave, hovers on the crest and then falls down the back of the sea on her side, the bending strain on the centreboard, which is transmitted to the case, must be terrific. The installation of the centreboard case, therefore, cannot be too strong and if allowance is made for this and the construction is carried out by the builder as planned, there should be no cause for constant leaking.

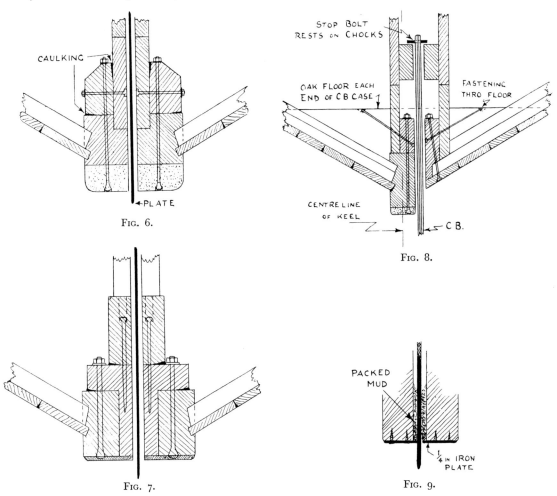

FIG. 6.

FIG. 8.

FIG. 7.

FIG. 9.

There are many ways of building a case on to the keel, and in very small craft such as sharpies and dinghies the construction can be of the simplest ; but in a cruiser which is planned to sail in hard weather without leaking a strong construction with rabbets and bolts is essential. Fig. 6 shows one method which is fairly common and has proved satisfactory, while Fig. 7 is a slight modification which can be maintained virtually leak proof. In Fig. 8 is the arrangement used by a large number of American work boats and coasting schooners, and by Mr. David

Hillyard of Littlehampton, Sussex, in his standard 24, 30 and 40 ft. centreboard chine yachts. In this the centreboard slot is cut in one of the garboards, not through the keel. Contrary to weakening the strakes this construction actually strengthens the garboards while it has the added advantages that (1) the keel is not cut into and (2) the tendency of ordinary centreboard yachts to have stones and mud jam in the bottom of the keel slot is prevented. Both the board and the case are slightly offset, but this is not any real disadvantage, and I do not see any defects at all in this arrangement, which has so far worked perfectly.

A method which has often been suggested for preventing small stones from being forced up into the slot and jamming the plate is to bolt iron plates underneath the keel, giving about $\frac{1}{8}$ in. clearance for the centreplate (Fig. 9). This keeps out pebbles, it is true, but it still does not prevent soft mud from being forced up inside the case when the boat settles tide after tide, and drying into a solid caked mass which equally effectively jams the centreplate up. It is better then not to have the close fitting plates but rather to allow about $\frac{3}{4}$ in. of play for the plate in the keel slot, so that an iron slat or rod can be used to force out the mud and stones.

All these points may appear unnecessarily complicated when all one wants is a simple sliding keel, but like most things in life, a centreboard that is well planned and well done can be both useful and an asset, while a badly designed one can be the very devil. It is in order to improve the breed of shallow draught centreboard yachts that I have insisted on attention to these details.

And now I should like to quote at some length what Mr. Howard I. Chapelle of Wollaston, Mass., the author of *American Sailing Craft, Yacht Designing and Planning* and other books, and an acknowledged authority on centreboard craft, has written to me on this subject of the installation of centreboards and of their design :

' In dealing with the design and construction of the centreboard itself (writes Mr. Chapelle) I think the following construction is undoubtedly the most practical : First, the end blocks should be carried through the keel at each end of the slot. The lowest timber of the case, the log, should be about twice or two-and-a-half times the thickness of the centreboard case sides and should be carried up fairly high. The pivot of the centreboard case should either be in this log or above it so that the centreboard cannot swing down and out of the case if the lanyard breaks. It is a great mistake to put the pivot of the centreboard outside of the rabbet in the deadwood for this reason.

' There is some disagreement as to whether the next timber above the log should be thicker than the remaining planks of the case, particularly when the pivot bolt is above the log. Off-hand, I should say that the ideal construction would be to have the timber above the log of larger scantling than the remaining timbers of the case sides if the pivot bolt is above the log. Nevertheless, I have seen and inspected a large number of commercial craft in which the pivot bolt is above the log, yet the timber through which it passes was no thicker than the remaining timbers in the sides of the case.

' Where it is possible, the end blocks should be carried above the top of the case to the cabin roof or to the deck beams, particularly the forward end block. The top of the case itself should be covered with a piece of plank which should be easily removable to inspect the case and centreboard.

'I like to see the centreboard case bed, or log, bolted to the keel with a sheet of wicking between the log and the keel and also with the hold-down bolts having nuts and washers of good dimensions; the nuts inside so that they may be taken up on with a heavy wrench occasionally. In this way occasional pull on the wrench will keep the centreboard case log tight. This is very cheap construction and very practical.

'The lanyard should be of chain, without doubt, or an iron rod should be used. I do not think there is any form of centreboard superior to that in which the lanyard is at the after end of the board and in which the board is approximately rectangular in profile. This seems to prevent the board from being strained; and I have observed that the board is less inclined to warp or twist than when any other form is used.

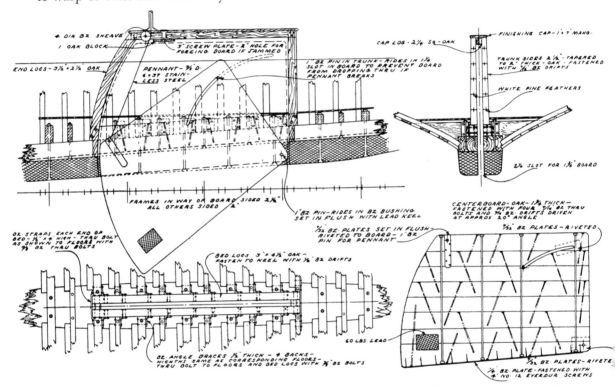

Construction details of a typical centreboard installation in a 39-ft. American cruising sloop. (Plans by Mr. Frederick C. Geiger of Philadelphia, see design on page 117). Note the oak end logs of the case continued through the keel, the splines (or feathers) in the planking of the case, the construction of the 1¾ in. oak board, the radius slot in board with 1 in. bronze stop bolt to prevent board falling right down, and the 60-lb. lead sinker set in board.

'I am wholly convinced, after a number of recent inspections, that both the L-shaped board and boards underneath the cabin floor are undesirable in wooden cruising yachts—at least, in our waters and in warm waters in general. The L-shaped board so popular in England seems to have a great tendency to twist and warp, due I think, to the strains set up in the arm. The only type of board I would recommend is one having its lanyard at the after end and pivoted, its forward end and its top brought up above the waterline, the case being capable of being opened for inspection. In waters where worms are bad it is good practice, by the way, to take the boat into smooth water, preferably fresh water, and to pour a couple of gallons of coal oil (kerosene) into the case and to allow the oil to stand in the case at least 24 hours. The oil will remain in the case and impregnate all around the waterline level to such an extent that worms will lose all taste for the wood. It is an excellent preservative and a very simple, inexpensive method of protecting the case from worms of all kinds. It is not necessary, I should say, to haul the boat out as the water will keep the oil in the case until the boat is put in motion or the water becomes disturbed.

' I like to have the centreboard pivot bolt of iron as it stands wear much better than composition or copper. However, in this country they have recently developed a composition metal called " Everdur ", which is a very hard bronze alloy suitable for screws and nails. This material would be excellent for the pivot bolt as it will stand wear as well as iron.

' As I wrote you some years ago, I think metal centreboards are impractical and wholly undesirable, and I also suggested that most centreboards employed in yachts are much too small and far too short. I believe that a centreboard should be of wood, make up of oak, edge bolted and dowelled together with a bit of lead ballast to sink it, and the board should be quite thick. A 40 ft. hull should have a board somewhere between 2 in. and 3 in. in thickness. The lower edge and the after edge may well be tapered off to get streamlines effect even if a thick board is used, though I do not believe that this adds appreciably to the speed of a cruising yacht.

' Returning to the construction of the case, there is one more thing I would like to mention —that is, the use of splines in the seams of the case. If the sides of the case are reasonably thick it is probably unnecessary to use splines as there is plenty of timber to caulk against. However, it is considered good yachting practice to employ splines though very rarely are splines found along the blocks. These splines are usually of hardwood and are rabbetted in to the plank on both sides of the seam at about half their thicknesses in from the outside of the case.

' In regard to the pivot bolt, I prefer good galvanized wrought iron pivot bolts and bearing in the board to bronze or copper. I will confess, however, that this is probably a matter of personal preference, as some of the better bronzes are certainly stronger.

' It is not unusual in our commercial craft for the crew to unship the board while the vessel is still afloat. There are various methods of doing this. The procedure is about as follows : Two plugs are first whittled out to be inserted in the pivot bolt holes when the pivot bolt has been knocked out. A line is passed underneath the hull at the fore end of the board to support it while the bolt is being removed. After the bolt has been cleared, the plugs are quickly inserted in the holes to stop the resulting leaks. The board is then dropped clear of the case by means of the line underneath the hull and the lanyard. Very often the board will float up alongside as soon as it is clear of the case. If the board will not float it may then be hooked from outside the hull by means of a long boat hook and hauled to the surface.

' The lanyard is unshackled and secured outside the hull while the board is being repaired or rebuilt. When the board is ready to be replaced in the case it is reshackled to its lanyard, and by means of guide lines, hauled underneath the hull and worked up into the case. If a board is very heavy it will not float. This operation is very easy. By means of the line underneath the hull at the fore end of the board, it is possible to work the board up so that the pivot bolt may be replaced without undue difficulty.

'In our schooners, particularly among commercial craft, it is not uncommon to find the centreboard either alongside the keel, off-centre, or the mainmast off-centre with the centreboard on the centreline. In a vessel of about 70 ft. long that I inspected this fall, the mainmast was apparently about 18 in. off-centre. As far as I could learn this had no effect on the sailing qualities of the vessel. I think, in a centreboard boat of any size, say about 40 ft. waterline, it would be a great saving to locate the board off-centre alongside the keel as this would avoid the necessity of paying the premium for wide timber to use in building up the keel to the proper width for a centre installation.

'Another advantage of the off-centre installation in the board, particularly in the schooners, is that it enables the designer to locate the position of the mainmast with more regard to proper balance of weights and centres.

'In the larger schooners it is not unusual to find the centreboard lanyard replaced by a wrought iron rod with a crotch, its lower end pinned to the top of the board at the after end and an eye at the upper end of the rod. This rod is located either just before or alongside the mainmast ; and the board is raised by a light tackle secured to the eye of the rod. When the board is up the eye is well aloft, almost to the cross-trees, and as the board is lowered, the eye of the rod descends. This has the advantage of keeping the gear off the deck in loading cargo. I have never seen this method employed in yachts, but there is certainly no reason why it should not serve with advantage.

'Generally speaking, the hull types most suitable for centreboard installation should have some forefoot but with moderate overhang at the bow, and the midsection should show some flare above the waterline as well as a reasonable amount of deadrise. I am referring, of course, to cruising boats.

'There is one criticism of English boats that I would like to make, and that is in regard to the shape of the counter. I think there is a tendency to carry the counter up too high and too thin, having too small a transom, in short. I think it would be better in a centreboard boat to have a transom more like our fishermen, rather deep and the counter immersed. I also think that it is quite desirable to carry the side well fore and aft, that is, not to have too curved a deck plan in a centreboard boat. As you know, I am somewhat sceptical of the practical application of all balancing methods. While they are helpful they are not sure methods of obtaining good design. I would rather resort to more or less dead-flat to obtain good balance for this reason, and I think it is particularly desirable to have this balance in a centreboard boat.

'I am trying to retain an open mind in regard to the various balancing methods, both the one proposed by Admiral Turner and the one I suggested in the pages of the *Yachting Monthly* sometime ago ; but I feel that the facts taken into consideration are too slight and too narrow in scope to give sound results. It is also my feeling that too enthusiastic an adoption of either theory might develop designs having far greater faults than now existing—due to lack of theoretical balance. I might add, that bad steering might come from a great many things besides longitudinal balance. I also feel that there has been too much emphasis placed upon these methods of finding balance to the exclusion of employing semi-dead-flat in the lines.

'I know that not all designers will agree with me in these ideas. Nevertheless, I have noticed that our best centreboard craft meet these requirements in nearly every case. To my mind, one of the best types that could be developed among yachts would be a moderately deep centreboard hull having a fair amount of her displacement in ballast, either inside or partly inside and out. It happens that the centreboard schooner type appeals to me personally, but there is no reason why a centreboard hull could not be used with any rig.

' Now, in regard to displacement, I think that a compromise hull having a little outside ballast, a good deal of deadrise and moderate displacement, combined with a centreboard, is the highest development of the centreboard type so far as cruisers are concerned. While it may be necessary to design what you call " barge yachts " and what we call " skipjacks " or " sharpie yachts " they are certainly types of purely local value and are not suitable for general cruising. I would like to see the sections of such yachts to have a good deal of deadrise, moderately hard bilges and flaring sides above the waterline. It is also desirable in some cases to have slightly hollow garboards. Perhaps in most designs it would be best to have all the ballast inside, but this is a matter of individual preference. I think a hollow waterline forward would be necessary in a centreboard of this type if there is to be desirable amount of forefoot, but I would hesitate to make a dogmatic statement to that effect.

' I do not think it is necessary to have a great deal of rake to the sternpost, by the way, though here again it is a matter of individual design rather than a fixed rule. It is also desirable, to my mind, to have a little more sheer than most English and American yachts employ in a good centreboard design, as such sheer tends to give greater rising power when knocked down.

' As to rigs of centreboard boats, I think any rig can be used, but there is one point to be kept in mind and that is that a centreboard boat is likely to be quick on her helm and, therefore, in designing the rig this should be taken into consideration. I think the rig of a cruising centreboarder can be very short on the base, but perhaps it would be better from the standpoint of handiness, to have a long base. This is a matter which I have not formed a definite opinion upon as yet, for a long base would increase the rapidity in which a centreboard boat comes around (it might be undesirable in so sensitive a type in many cases). On the other hand, the long base is subject to better balance in a sensitive boat for the same reason that a long keel benefits steady steering. I am not being very clear on this, I see; but the point is that length has a beneficial effect upon steering whether it is in the air or in the water. This thought requires more attention than I have been able to give it at the moment ; and I suggest it merely as a line of reasoning to be brought to your attention.'

III

Mainly about Editing and Education

'Knowledge comes, but wisdom lingers'—Tennyson

Moralists who follow certain curious lines of thought would have us believe that the world was never so wicked nor so cruel as it is today : that people are more selfish and callous to each other than they ever were, while war is infinitely more barbaric now than it was in olden times.

I cannot subscribe to this belief. To take the last first : horrors of ancient warfare were very real ; showers of deadly vipers, of Greek fire, of poisoned darts and boiling oil were but minor tortures inflicted on both sides, while the unbelievable cruelties enacted on the populations of besieged cities, as in the fall of Carthage or Troy and the Inca strongholds, with their deliberate spreading of pestilence and disease, their massacres and tortures, were every whit as bad, to my mind, as the modern air raid or gas attack.

In peace time I believe white races on the whole tend to be more humane, more tolerant and more sensible of pain than they were even a few generations back. With all its faults when the wrong people have acquired knowledge, universal education, which after all is still but a generation or two old, has given all people, the poorest as well as the middle class, an awareness of the feelings of others, a consciousness that pain or hurt or injustice inflicted on another without cause is wrong, just as thieving or any form of crime against the community is fundamentally wrong. Through education alone—not just schooling, but through the far reaching results of published literature, of broadcasting, of an awareness of public opinion— there is, I am convinced, a better standard of behaviour in all classes to their fellow men than there was at the time of the Reform Bill. Crowds on the whole would appear to be better behaved than they were even eighty years ago, and I feel certain, to take just one instance, that had it been possible to put present-day well-upholstered and furnished saloon railway coaches on trains back in the '40's, the third class passengers of that date would probably have ruined the interiors and removed all the fittings. Why ? And the position of the unaccompanied woman in trains, buses, hotels and streets, is vastly different from that of eighty or even forty years ago. Why ? Public opinion on the treatment of all helpless things, from dumb animals and birds to prisoners and property, has undergone a striking change within the past half century. Again why ? I think the answer is : Education.

I do not think for one moment that man is *happier* by much education : an educated man, it is said, is one who is able to worry about a lot of things that never trouble the ignorant. It must be admitted that education may have the effect of making bovine people of low mentality discontented with their lot, perhaps resentful to the world in consequence and only too ready to break up a régime that feeds them and clothes them but expects them to work ; it may turn the old Bill Sykes type of burglar into a smooth, cunning, well-read criminal ; and it may make

26

boys and girls in humble homes restless and ruthless in their desire to gain what the world of talking films dangles before them. Nothing in this world is without its disappointments or its man-made mistakes, but education does improve the people as a race, it does build up in time a better community.

As an aside : If you don't believe that, why take a look at America and think how dull life would be in its cities if there had never been prohibition, co-education, advertising campaigns, the R. C. A., or negro emancipation !

Though it may sound like a descent from the sublime to the ridiculous, from the grim world of reality to the comfortable realm of sport, the yachting press has done much for the education of the yachtsman over a number of years. Ever since I took over the editorial side, twelve years ago, of the little publication *Yacht Sales and Charters* and was later transferred to the *Yachting Monthly* when the two were amalgamated, a deliberate policy of educating its readers to the greater and wider possibilities of their sport has been followed. Probably few of our readers realized with what care every article, every feature, almost every picture and drawing was chosen, perhaps only to be rewritten or altered so that its presence was justified on the grounds that it taught at least one new lesson. I have never accepted articles or stories because they were written by friends of mine and, unlike the unenviable position of some editors, my directors have never questioned my decision nor asked me to publish anything submitted by their friends against my judgment. For a dozen years this has been my editorial policy—not an easy one, for it needs a firm hand and an honest belief in one's own decisions—but when, a few weeks before this was written, the firm's auditors examined a recent questionnaire scheme and announced that, covering almost every country in the world, the *Yachting Monthly* had over 20,000 readers—more than three times the number a decade previously—it seemed that the policy of education was being appreciated.

Learning, it is said, begins when we realize how little we know. I remember, when I was a very new and young editor—twenty-four to be exact—and struggling with the many problems and new angles on old difficulties that the ordinary reader cannot see nor the general public suspect, overhearing two even younger and perhaps callower youths at an adjoining table in a restaurant. They were telling two young women about a holiday on the Broads.

' Why there's nothing in sailing,' exclaimed one, ' it's as simple as A.B.C. Before we shoved off the man just told us how to set the sails, and at the end of the week we'd learnt all there is to know about it ! '

Fortunately sailing is not quite as simple as that. True, sailing a modern Broads hired yacht—a type of boat which is perfect for her purpose—is the simplest form of sailing, provided the Broads are not too crowded. But it is to deep water cruising, to handling sea-going yachts in tidal waters, to seamanship in fact, as riding a ' Dodgem ' car at a fun fair is to good driving on the roads.

If that youth sailed again on salt water instead of the placid Broads, his education as a seaman would only begin when he began to understand how much more there was to know, to appreciate the saying that it takes several years for anyone to learn to handle a yacht reasonably well, and a lifetime to admit how much more there is to learn. This Way of Life termed cruising in small craft embraces a very large field of knowledge, and those older men who have devoted the greater part of their lives to its study have acquired a knowledge that embraces weather lore and sky and clouds, a knowledge of deep water and shallow seas, of tides and winds and currents, of astronomy and geometry in navigation, of ropes and ropework, of canvas, sails, rigging, paints and varnishes, of timber and its infinite variations, of wood preservatives and decay, of theory in the designs of boats and their construction . . . in short, many subjects that competent seamen can discuss for hours without touching on the one thing our young Broads visitor knew all about—the actual sailing.

It was overhearing a chance conversation in a tube train soon after I had joined *Yacht Sales and Charters* that gave me the idea that proved the germ from which the Little Ship Club was to spring a year later. Two quite normal-looking men who were obviously going to their respective offices were talking about rigs and ropes and canvas for small cruisers and I felt right then that it was a pity all the salty-minded young men who either owned or dreamed of owning small boats could not meet each other at some club or house in London just to exchange yarns and ideas. An editorial in the little bi-weekly that I did for the next issue—it was in November 1925—suggesting such a club for London's cruising-minded men raised some interest, but I had my hands too full to give much more thought to it, and it was not until Tony Gibbons, owner of a handsome ex-pilot cutter *Seabreeze*, repeated the suggestion in a letter which was published several months later, and a room at the Old Ship Tavern in the Whitehall end of the Charing Cross Road was offered by the proprietor, that a nucleus of the Little Ship Club was formed. Today its membership extends to many countries and exceeds 1,200, and it gives a service to the average cruising man that few other clubs have ever given, although a number have come to acknowledge their cruising members and copied the idea.

Those were interesting days after the launching of *Yacht Sales and Charters* from the *Yachting Monthly* offices. Looking back now I can scarcely believe what little practical advice or assistance was then available to the uninitiated small boat owner, the impecunious owner of the little 6-tonner, the converted lifeboat, or the smack. None of the yacht clubs had any room for him, most of them recognized yachting as either class racing or one-design sailing, and only one or two old-established cruising institutions gave their members such help as special charts, pilotage advice and a useful library. Few books of any practical value to the small boat owner had been written. There was Claud Worth's classic *Yacht Cruising*, but most of its valuable advice pertained to cruising yachts of a fair size and of an assumed standard of smartness far beyond the capabilities of the average week-end yachtsman or his slender income. One or two most helpful books had been written many years before by Knight and Cowper, while Francis B. Cooke's *Cruising Hints* was the most widely read, I believe, but there seemed to be little else. My own first effort, *Yachting on a Small Income*, which came out early in 1925, was written with the hope of dispelling the popular idea that it needed a lot of money to own any sort of boat that you could sleep in, and the little book sold in surprising numbers : in fact it had a thousand readers within quite a short time.

In those days the existing yachting press scarcely recognized the small cruiser, for as one manager explained to me : ' There's no money in the little yachts. Their owners spend next to nothing in the trade, and it's only the big yachts and their expensive crews and of course the advertising that goes with them, that enable yachting papers to exist at all.' At that time he was probably quite right : it was indeed a great struggle to publish any yachting paper under reasonable conditions, and the staffs were all hard worked and badly underpaid. The fact that there was a comparatively large potential public amongst men who as yet owned no boats but merely dreamed of the day when they would be able to—frequently the most enthusiastic readers of yachting papers—had not been recognized.

Against all advice and precedent, therefore, *Yacht Sales and Charters* was launched and for a stormy two years I managed the editorial side. The readers' response was immediate and very gratifying, letters poured in from almost all over the world, from sea-hungry exiles in places we had to search for in the office atlas, and all of them said in effect the same thing : ' It is the paper we cruising and small boat chaps have been waiting for.' Given a free hand, I just gave the readers what I felt they wanted, for my own early days of sailing were not far astern, and the two previous grim years as a struggling free lance writer in London, when with no money and no friends I had never had quite enough to eat and had lived from day to day, miserable and desperately anxious, wondering whether I should ever possess a boat of my own again, were still fresh in my mind. One does not forget such things very easily.

The sales of the little paper went up and up and its parent publication began to feel its effect. Then it began to dawn on us that this was not enough. The advertisers were not anxious to buy space in a paper, whatever its circulation, when that circulation apparently consisted only of impecunious owners of little boats, ' toreouts ' and ' riz-ons ', or of persons who owned no boat at all. It was a shock to learn that papers existed far more on the revenue from the advertisement pages that they could sell than on the number of copies bought, and that to those with the paper's finance at heart the number of advertisement pages was of far greater moment than the most brilliant editorial coup. At the time it seemed a cruel blow to one's ideals : running a yachting paper was evidently not to be all pleasure and kindness, but grim Business.

For a time I thought failure stared us in the face—failure with the most enthusiastic body of readers asking for more and more ! But the fortunes of the parent magazine, the *Yachting Monthly*, had not been improving since its original editor, Herbert Reiach, had died five years before, and it was this that had given the junior fortnightly upstart its chance. With its absorption by the *Yachting Monthly* I was given the editorial control of the combined papers and set out with a determination to keep all my old readers, all the *Monthly's* old readers and to make it such an all-round good magazine for yachtsmen and those who loved the sea that they would *all* just have to read it.

We had our troubles, my goodness ! Internal ones that brought rapid changes to the staff for a year or two until we settled down ; troubles with old contributors who were incensed at the change in editorial policy and the resulting ' printed politenesses ' ; quarrels with the advertisement department who demanded editorial ' puffs ' for their clients ; skirmishes with advertisers who bought space and afterwards would not pay for it ; difficulties in an office where new methods and some orderly system had to be devised for keeping the many cross-indexes of contributors and contents, reading the MSS., dealing with the block orders, the proofs, the endless correspondence, the ' Can you advise me ? ' letters, the 'phone queries, the tracing of badly drawn plans, the interviewing of callers, the planning of the next-number-but-one, the writing of the trade notes and news items, the sifting of advice or abuse as it poured in by the mail ; and the frequent arguments with printers, block makers and paper manufacturers. Sometimes I have returned home exhausted from a heavy day at the office, too tired to face the pile of MSS. that I had planned to read after dinner and remembered with amusement friends' remarks ' I've always wondered what an editor really *did*.'

I remember how on press days I used to hurry across Hungerford Bridge to the works of our old printers, looking wistfully down the Thames at the tugs and lighters and barges, wondering when I should get time to indulge in the game I loved so much instead of trying only to write about it amid the turmoil of a busy office. Those visits to the printers were a splendid grounding for any young editor or writer, for they taught one some of the difficulties under which a printer had to work, mechanical ones as well as human, and always in a rush against time. In shirt sleeves I used to read through the final proofs, still tacky with ink from the press, marvelling at the mistakes that one still occasionally found after the paper had been ' put to bed '—for proof reading is a specialized work and few people are really good at it ; I had to cut articles that had trailed a paragraph or two over their allotted space, write captions under blocks that had been mislaid and reappeared at the last moment, and occasionally would be forced to rearrange that jig saw puzzle called the ' make up ' while the foreman printer dashed in and out, running his hands through greying hair : ' Mr. Griffiths, for God's sake let us have that last proof. The boy's finished the make-ready and the machine's waiting. . . .' ' In a moment, Mr. Spinks, you've got the wrong block set in here.' ' Oh, my God. . . .'

I liked to see what work it entailed for the printer when the thoughtless editor changed his layout and rearranged some photographs on the page ; I liked to learn just what a business it can be when one of the boys dropped a forme (a steel frame) and scattered the lead type all over the floor, and how when this happened after the final proofs had been passed its remaking might contain many errors which would puzzle the innocent reader and bring indignant letters from others pointing out the error.

Sometimes I would stay when my work was through and watch the machines begin their long run : I liked the heavy rhythmic thunder of their going, the flash of the white sheets as they were fed under the rollers, the sickly, exciting smell of the ink, and the general air of hurry, hurry that throbbed throughout the building. And the process department where the blocks were made—in those days our printers also made our blocks—was a fascinating series of dark rooms, with their zinc baths and shaded blue lights and silent figures etching new plates with deft fingers, and the all-pervading pungent smell of the acids.

Many a time I used to walk back over the bridge very late at night, tired to exhaustion, yet happy to be a part of such a complicated system, and to be responsible for the magazine that was destined to be read by sea-hungry men in every part of the Empire.

Later, when we changed to a printing works at Bedford—50 miles from London—we had organized the matter of going to press and the general running of the editorial department to such effect that it became unnecessary for anyone to put the paper to bed at the printers ; with a rigid time schedule, a strong hand on late contributors and no muddling it is now done entirely in the office, and the printers are never kept waiting at the last moment. But I still enjoy an occasional visit to an efficient printing works, to listen to the throb of the machines, to see the foreman printer handling his hourly problems, to smell the ink once more. . . .

MAINLY ABOUT EDITING AND EDUCATION

It is an exciting work editing a periodical in which you have your heart and much of your ambition, for each number goes forth as a little part of yourself, a little piece of creative work over which you and your assistants have spent many hours of thought and planning ; and it is good to feel that it will go to the far corners of the earth, to bring something of interest, something new, some remembrance of the sea, of sailing, of the way of life we call cruising, to thousands of men who look for its green cover each month with the expectation of a few happy hours. No two yachtsmen may be quite in agreement over the contents that they like most ; the keen racing men may feel hurt because their thrilling Saturday afternoon contests in the local one-designs have not been reported ; some of the advertisers may wish the small boat owner to blazes and look for references only to the most expensive type of yachting ; other might-be advertisers may be disappointed at their failure to gain free puffs for their wares ; and the theory fiends may deprecate the space ' wasted ' on cruising yarns while the cruising men pull faces at the columns ' wasted ' on theory of yacht design ; but on the whole the yachting community—by which is meant the sailing, racing, cruising, motor boating and even theorizing yachtsmen—is an appreciative and happy community to work for.

Occasionally, when I become tired and stale, and tell myself that I'm sick to death of writing, talking and thinking about yachts, that I want to go right away, forget the continuous monthly editorial schedule, forget boats and meet fresh people who won't even mention them, and wonder whether I shall grow old and cantankerous like so many men in my profession, I appeal to an old friend who lives a calmer life than mine, albeit he is a much travelled man of letters.

His reply is always soothing and usually on the same lines : " Don't I know that utter weariness of the spirit ? That fear that the mental spring, the ideas, the very *zest* for it all will dry up ? You, my dear Maurice, have been working too long and too hard, and you are suffering from a competition complex. Everything is all right, really it is. Are there not lovely little ships now sailing whose origin was your own designing table ? Are not your three yachting books bringing interest and knowledge—and I would say delight—to hundreds—let us hope thousands—of boat-minded men and women ? You only need a rest. Go away, tell your assistant to bring out the next issue, and don't come back till you *want* to. And you will.'

And I do. But I fear this is a long diversion from the real subject of these little ships.

Slowly but surely yachtsmen in this country are being educated above the old-fashioned ideas of their grandparents. While the heavy, over-sparred yachts that figure so picturesquely in old prints are admitted to have been exceedingly comfortable at sea, the necessity for such deep draught, so much ballast, such heavy displacement, such great sail plans has latterly been questioned, and, following the lead of their transatlantic cousins, they are coming to recognize the moderate or light displacement, shoal draught boat with an efficient rig and a capable auxiliary motor, as far more suited to the needs of the modern owner with limited time.

IV

The Layout depends on Circumstances

I DON'T know whether learner-pilots in the Air Force are given to wanting to design their own aeroplanes, or 'L' drivers their own ideal motor car, but such precocity is no worse than the inexperienced yachtsman's attempts to design the ideal cruiser.

Before building a cruising yacht, however complete one thinks one's ideas are for the dream-ship, it is always wise to buy a second-hand boat (the exact type is not important) and to go out and cruise in her. Never mind if she is not a bit like the dream-ship you imagine : the very difficulties into which you will get her, the accidents that may happen to her rigging and gear, the mess that she gets into below decks after a dusting at sea, the faults in her rig or layout that will only become obvious under sea conditions; in short, the actual handling of her week-end after week-end will not only prove valuable experience, but will open the mind to fresh ideas and probably reveal the intended dream-ship in a far less perfect light. There is nothing like actual contact with the sea, the tides, the winds, the mud and the forces of nature to show up the futility of inexperienced theories and the absurdities talked in the bars of most yacht clubs.

It has been said—by a yachtsman's wife, I suspect—that yachting people are a quarrelsome lot. I expect golfers, huntsmen, polo players, even dart throwers and bowls players, occasionally come under the same argumentative category. But of yachtsmen it is quite true. Amongst the racing classes the squabbles that rage in club houses after the race are notorious, while I have seen genuine feuds result between members, and even groups of members, on account of some technical offence at a mark buoy. The smaller the boats, it would seem, the bigger the squabbles, the higher pitched are the catty comments of the keen racing ladies and the deeper the canine growls of the serious racing men. This may appear very absurd, but, heaven knows, even the international matches for the *America's* Cup in past years have not been without their own growls and bites !

Amongst the cruising people perhaps a little more tolerance is noticeable, because they are not generally thrown together in a purely competitive spirit so often as the racing combatants, nor are they so prone to stop speaking to one another, to ignore each other's presence when they meet in the club or to think that other fellow ' devoid of all decency and sportsmanship, pah ! ' But, given the opportunity, the keen cruising man delights in trying to show the other fellow how wrong he is in his ideas about rigs or engines or bowsprits or overhangs, and since no two yachtsmen, to my knowledge, have been known to agree entirely over every single feature in any design for a yacht, the planning of a cruising boat opens up an infinity of ideas and alternatives.

I have listened, for example, for hours to arguments on the best rig for a cruising boat, wondering at the temperatures that were generated beneath perfectly respectable collars while otherwise jovial and kind hearted yachtsmen banged the table and glared at each other like

32

THE LAY-OUT DEPENDS ON CIRCUMSTANCES

H. M. Bateman's apoplectic colonels. I have waited politely to insert a suggestion into a three-cornered argument on the best place for the galley, but without a chance to get in edgeways. I have seen two otherwise respectable yachtsmen—for all one knows, kind fathers, good citizens and amiable husbands—who have been growling at one another after a few remarks on the relative advantages of rigging screws or lanyards and dead eyes. As more than one yacht building firm has discovered to its cost, it is impossible to produce a small cruising yacht which will suit the requirements of any one yachtsman in every particular, while everyone who buys will want alterations made to suit his own ideas. And it is these slight alterations that prevent mass production methods from being made full use of in boats, and drive up the cost of building.

Many yachtsmen like to think that there is only one proper way of arranging or doing anything aboard a boat, one suitable rig, one best place for the galley, one good arrangement for the saloon, the fo'c'sle, the pantry, the clothes locker, the lavatory or the engine, and that all the others are mistakes. Such men are generally satisfied and content with their own boats and probably keep them half their lives, but they are hopeless to discuss boats with, for their invariable remark ends with, ' Well, no one has been able to improve on my boat yet : I've had her thirty years, and I don't want anything better.' And that finishes the subject.

So many yachtsmen unfortunately cannot see why others prefer a different type of boat from their own : many enthusiasts for long overhangs and ' all inboard ' rigs cannot imagine why there are still men who find much to favour in plumb ended boats and the old style of gaff rig. They just regard the others as fools who have not yet seen the light, and leave it at that. And, of course, the plumb-ended, ' all boat ' men just feel that these modern boats with their short keels and long snouts are all wrong and have only come into vogue because a gang of young bloods who ought to have known better found they would stand hard driving and could win races without actually drowning their crews.

While owning a dozen boats in all I have tried to keep an open mind on questions of design, rig, lay out and so forth, and to refrain from laying down the law concerning them in the pages of the *Yachting Monthly.* For it is clear to me that there is no law to be laid down. Every change in hull form, in rigging details, in the sail plan, in accommodation, in the hundred and one alterable details of a yacht's equipment, has its own reasons, its own advantages, its own disadvantages, its own adherents and its critics : virtually nothing which has been put into a yacht with forethought is entirely good or entirely bad. (This sounds like Lincoln's Gettysburg address, doesn't it ?)

As an example let us take the galley, about the position of which boat owners are ready to argue till it's ' Time gentlemen, *please* ! ' You go aboard a boat of, say, 12 tons or 30 ft. water-line and say, ' Well, I like her, but the galley would have been better aft.' Now, why ? This owner plans to carry a paid hand who will occupy the fo'c'sle. The hand will be expected to do all the cooking, washing-up and chores. The galley, with its smells of boiling fat and greens and onions and soups, in this case is best forward, for while at anchor the draught in a small yacht almost invariably flows from aft forward and not from forward aft. With the pantry and sink the galley in a boat with a paid hand, then, is better out of the way forward so that the saloon and the sleeping cabin may be undisturbed before and after meals for the owner and his wife and guests.

33

' But ', you say, ' if he makes a lengthy voyage, is it a good place then, right forward ? '

I say, no it is not. You say, then what *do* you mean if just now you said forward *was* the best place for the galley ? And I take a breath and answer that it may work well even there if the hand can cook a hot meal with the ship lifting the pots off the stove as she plunges. I have known some excellent hands aboard small cruisers who have insides like iron and willing dispositions, and who make no objection to working their way forward in a plunging, heeling little ship in order to get a hot meal for the owner and his friends. But if the owner does the cooking himself at sea the galley is more convenient if placed just aft of the midship section, where the motion is least violent.

' That's where I'd always put it,' you say, with a triumphant gleam.

Quite a good place, I agree, for deep water cruisers and for boats whose owners not only plan to be, but actually are, at sea for days at a time. The pots and pans don't get thrown about so much with the galley near the pivotal point about which the yacht pitches, and it is not nearly such a dangerous and difficult journey for one to make from the cockpit. Many a good intention has been lost on its way to the stuffy fo'c'sle of a wildly pitching little cruiser. But the galley just under the main hatch at the foot of the companion still has its disadvantages in, say, a 10-tonner. The draught still comes straight down on to the stove and may make lighting a Primus a difficult operation ; the smell of frying and boiling greens still drifts forward and permeates the ship, the cook himself is frequently very much in the way at the bottom of the companion steps for those who go in and out of the cabin, while he rarely has ample shelf space on which to rest hot plates, dishes, saucepans of water or cooking utensils.

Personally I consider the galley is best placed aft in any little boat up to 9 or 10 tons (say 28 ft. waterline) after which it becomes an advantage to have it at the forward end of the saloon, perhaps in a separate lobby between the saloon and the fo'c'sle, and then in boats of 16 or 18 tons and over with a regular paid hand, the galley and pantry are probably most convenient when placed near the mast and separated from the saloon and sleeping quarters by a good bulk-head.

In my 9 ton shallow draught cutter *Nightfall*, which I owned from 1931 until 1935, the galley was originally in the fo'c'sle. All meals in consequence had to be brought aft through a low and narrow door, and when beating to windward it was almost impossible to endure the atmosphere in the forecastle and cook at the same time. This arrangement, however, suited the previous owner who had had her built. He never did any fierce off-shore cruising in her but preferred leisurely pottering, and he almost invariably carried a paid hand. The hand did the cooking where he slept, in the fo'c'sle, and passed the plates and food through the door into the cabin.

But I have never carried a paid hand and I soon found the doubled-up journey in and out of the fo'c'sle door with plates and dishes very inconvenient, and it was not long before I moved the galley into a 2 ft. 6 in. long lobby abaft the mast, where the forward end of the coachroof gave standing headroom, the four opening ports light and air, and the position less violent motion.

Almost the same arrangement was copied when I designed my 10-tonner *Wild Lone II*, and whether singlehanded or with one or two guests aboard I have found this location convenient

34

and quite satisfactory for a boat of this size. The galley is close to the saloon table, yet its smells are taken forward, it is near enough to the pivotal point of the ship to have almost the minimum motion, and the cook is not in the way of the rest of the crew.

It is impossible, however, to generalize or to lay down the law even about such a simple matter as the placing of the galley : what suits one owner or one set of conditions will not necessarily be acceptable to another.

This, I think, is where so many yachtsmen make a mistake in drawing up an exacting set of requirements when they approach a professional naval architect for a new design. I am well aware that there are one or two professional yacht designers whose personal experience at sea of the yachts they design and of the various ideas they embody in the planning of interiors is, to say the least of it, a little lacking, but on the whole the experienced and competent professional naval architect has usually forgotten more than the average amateur has yet learnt, and it is generally to the owner's own advantage if he states a few essential requirements—perhaps even submits a rough sketch of his ideas—and then gives the designer a free hand.

It would be thought, for instance, that there was only one ' best ' position for the toilet aboard, say, a boat 30 ft. on the waterline. Not a bit of it. Some owners like the w.c. to be hidden in a cramped, airless cubby hole near the mast, so that (*sotto voce*) ' the ladies can use it ' when they are aboard. As if they would when the rest of the crowd are in the saloon or someone is in the forecastle ! One owner of a 35-footer insisted against my own suggestions on having the toilet at the foot of the main companion where it was so cramped it even cramped one's style. He quite forgot that its use was obvious to anyone either in the cockpit or in the saloon, and was most unpopular with his more timid friends. After a season he had the toilet moved into the forecastle where at least the most retiring guest could imagine herself in seclusion, and the space at the main companion made a fine clothes locker.

As in the case of the galley, the location of the toilet depends on how many people are planned to cruise aboard, whether they are a mixed party or not (and if so how mixed), or whether the forecastle will be occupied by a paid hand or one or two members of the party. For my own ship I prefer the w.c. to be in the forecastle, right forward, where it has ample light and air; it can be kept scrupulously clean, and when in use the saloon and the remainder of the ship can be shut right off. And if by chance the berth in the forecastle is occupied and someone of the opposite sex in the saloon wishes it were not, it is simple enough to have temporary arrangements in the cockpit—simpler, at least, than trying to be unobtrusive in an enclosed toilet between forecastle and saloon !

All this may appear to the amateur anxious to learn as a little bewildering, and I can imagine him settling a little lower into his collar and mumbling : ' Damn it all, there must *be* a best position for the galley or lavatory or the best arrangement below decks for, say, an 8 tonner. Why can't you say definitely what this is ? ' Many yachtsmen feel like that, and some decide that they have the one and only good lay-out or galley or saloon arrangement and believe that any alternative is just a waste of time and quite wrong. In touching on these vexed questions, therefore, I have tried to show how, as in most things in this world, there are several ways of doing things, and each is right for its own particular purpose.

As a final example take the question of sleeping berths in a small cruiser. Some men like a boat that is chock full of bunks and pseudo bunks and, in order to accommodate the droves of friends or offspring they intend to have on board, they fit cubbyhole bunks under the decks alongside the cockpit. These quarter berths have always been a feature in German yachts, but many yachtsmen and certainly most yachtswomen would not tolerate them because of the acrobatic difficulty in getting in or out of them and of the impossibility of ever airing them properly. Then, while some men like the main companion to lead into a sleeping cabin aft, others think this a mighty poor idea and say they just wouldn't go to sea in a yacht that hadn't got the sleeping cabin forward of the saloon and plenty of space for wet oilskins and seaboots right aft. And yet others declare that they wouldn't have a boat with a separate sleeping cabin anyway : if they had the space for one they would rather devote it to a decent engineroom and a large galley. So it is quite impossible to suit all tastes and reasons put forward with any particular type of boat or lay-out below decks, and to attempt to do so is an indication that one does not understand the various motives that lead men to buy boats.

V

The Meaning of 'Lines': and 'Tonnage'

YACHTSMEN on the whole nowadays have become so proficient in the art of 'reading' yachts' lines and understanding what is indicated by the various plans that go to make up a complete design—thanks to the educative efforts of the yachting press, combined with the designing classes and lectures arranged by a number of clubs in recent years—that I hesitate to offer a completely elementary explanation of the subject. I only hope that by means of these notes those who have not been able before to visualize the form of a hull from seeing

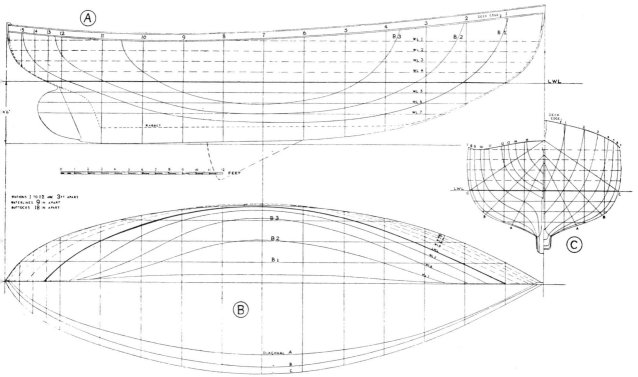

FIG. 1.—Lines of a 40 ft. by 11·5 ft. by 4·5 ft. draught C.B. cruising yacht to illustrate the meaning of the various lines described in the text.

the plans may be enabled to follow better the designs of shoal draught cruisers given later, while those who know all about it can skip this chapter without the slightest jolt to the conscience.

As an example for our purpose I have taken the lines of a 17 ton centreboarder which I had to design recently for a Dutch client. (Fig. 1). The lines are those of a normal hull for off-shore and estuary cruising on the Dutch and English coasts and the dimensions : LOA 40 ft., LWL 34 ft. 2 in., Beam 11 ft. 6 in., Draught 4 ft. 6 in., ex-C.B.

The lines are designed to show the builder just what shape the hull must be within the limits of these measurements, and they indicate the vessel from three points of view : broadside (elevation or sheer plan, A), from vertically underneath (half-breadth plan, B) and from end on (sections or body plan, C). And in each case the same lines will be found to tally exactly.

Plan A is the elevation or profile view of the hull which the builder lays down full size in chalk on his mould loft floor. From this he will get the exact curve of the stem for which a piece of oak—if it is to be oak—must be selected. Plan C is the end view of the boat, the body plan. As both sides of every boat are intended to be identical—although from the behaviour of some roughly built boats it may not always be so—only one side is shown, and in this body plan, the forward half from amidships—the biggest and fattest section—to the bow is shown on the right and the after half from amidships to the stern is shown on the left.

The horizontal line marked LWL is the Load Water Line, the position at which the designer intends (or hopes) that the vessel will float when fully loaded with her sails, rigging, gear, tanks full and her hull, in fact, in cruising trim. The LWL is the principal line from which nearly all the measurements are taken, yet such is the complete cussedness of everything to do with boats, it is most often the line which, in actual practice, is *not* where it appears on the plans. Most cruising yachts float an inch or two deeper than their designed LWL—some much more than that—while it is frequently found that a yacht's sea-going qualities and behaviour are improved if she is trimmed two or three inches by the stern—that is, put that much down aft below the designed LWL.

It will be seen that the elevation is cut into fifteen vertical lines called Sections or Stations. In this particular design numbers 1 to 12 are 36 in. apart, but this is no arbitrary measurement. You may either divide all your designs along the load waterline into ten or twelve equal parts, so that only the distance between each two sections varies according to the length of the LWL, or you may put in as many sections as you like. Some builders, when building with sawn oak frames, appreciate it if you place your sections where each of these frames will be : it simplifies the builder's work in making the moulds (or templates) from which to cut these frames exactly to shape.

How this is done is described in a later chapter. Moulds are usually made up of any odd pieces of wood, but their outer edges, giving the actual curve or section of the hull at that station, must tally accurately to the corresponding station or section on the plan. A 35-ft. yacht might be built around ten or twelve moulds (in a difficult stern, for example, like a canoe, three moulds at 12-in. spacing, as in this plan, might be wisely used), whereas most small dinghies are planked around only two moulds, one in the bow, the other amidships, while the transom virtually forms a third mould right aft. When the ship is planked up the moulds are removed, and either broken up or kept for building another similar vessel.

Now the actual shape of these moulds is shown in the body plan where one side (or half) of each one is indicated. If we imagined that we had an exact scale *half* model of this hull and with a saw cut neatly through the hull at right angles exactly at the places indicated by the numbers 1, 2, 3, 4, . . . then, looked at from either the bow end or the stern, the sawn faces would have exactly the shapes shown on the body plan and representing sections 1, 2, 3, 4, . . . end on.

Given the yacht's sheer plan from which the stem, the stern and the keel deadwoods could be cut and the sheer line of the deck reproduced, and given these sections from which the moulds can be made, a builder could build a hull which would be very nearly exactly as planned. Many fishing boat builders would be far happier with no more plans to worry them than that. But for the accurate work which is essential for yacht construction, some further check on the shape of the hull is needed, while an incomplete design can neither be read accurately nor may it reveal various defects which in the finished boat would result in failure.

We therefore have cuts at the hull from three more angles, resulting in waterlines, buttocks and diagonals.

The waterlines reveal the shape of the hull as it would appear from directly underneath—a fish's aspect, so to speak. The waterlines are spaced vertically at equal distances one above the other—in Plan A they are 9 in. apart. One could have had twice as many WL's by spacing them half that distance apart, but 9 in. for a boat of this size give enough WL's for building purposes. The shape of these WL's is revealed in the upper half of Plan B (remember, we are dealing with only one side or half of the hull : the other should be identical).

If the yacht were lowered cautiously by a crane until the water level reached WL 7 (the lowest one on the plan) and raised again so that we could walk underneath, the wetted part, not allowing for perspective, would look like the line WL 7 in Plan B. And if the yacht were lowered again so that she sank to each one of the other WL's in turn, in each case the wetted part would curve around her hull as shown by the corresponding waterlines in the upper half of Plan B.

Or if raising and lowering with a crane appears a cumbersome way of demonstrating the waterlines (you're telling me !) we can take horizontal saw cuts through our half model once again at the places marked by the

A drawing of a double-centreboard 80-ft. schooner chosen to show how the waterlines, sections, and buttock lines (shown pecked) appear in perspective. The hollow in the flaring bow sections, the flatness of the garboards amidships, the hollowness in the waterlines aft (the ' run') and the width of the quarters are all clearly indicated by the various lines. This old schooner was built about 1820, probably as a slaver, but later was used by the Navy in suppression of this trade in the West Indies, and the drawing comes from Howard I. Chapelle's *History of American Sailing Ships*.

WL's, and the slices when laid flat will show sawn faces corresponding to the WL's in the upper ha—oh, well, let the whole chorus finish the sentence.

So far so good, boys and girls. But the builder—or more likely the designer—will want to check up on the curves of the hull which come *between* these various saw cuts or lines. In the full size hull these spaces would be fairly large and quite liable to an error of $\frac{1}{2}$ in. or more in the curve given to the planking—an amount quite sufficient to affect a yacht's hull form considerably. It is true that, given accurately made moulds spaced at the right distances from stem to stern, there should not be very much wrong with the form of the hull, for although planking is obstinate when you try to bend it around bluff curves, it takes a good curve naturally. In itself a hull which is 'easy to plank' is usually a good hull, for where rigid planks can be made to go quite fairly the water will flow all the more easily. But this is not quite good enough to ensure the design's being followed exactly, or at least to within $\frac{1}{8}$ in. Indeed, it is surprising how much difference there would be in the hulls built by different builders to a set of lines which were incomplete for checking.

Two or more *vertical* cuts are therefore taken fore and aft parallel to the line of the keel and usually at equal distances apart. These are the buttock lines. The buttock lines (B 1, B 2, B 3) are shown in the example, all 18 in. apart.

If we take our saw and cut through the hull vertically along the outside buttock B 3, the sawn face of the piece that comes away should be shaped as the buttock line B 3 on the sheer plan (A). Similarly buttocks B 2 and B 1 represent saw cuts along these two buttock lines respectively. The importance of these buttock lines when reading a design will be explained later.

As a final check on the moulds or the accurate shape of the same frames, three, four or more diagonal cuts are taken at any place but generally so chosen that they will cut the hull surface or planking, roughly at right angles. Here again, if our saw is brought into play the sawn face of Diagonal A when laid flat would be the shape of Diagonal A in the lower half of Plan B, and the sawn shapes of Diagonals B and C are shown likewise. There is no fixed angle or position for the diagonals, but it will be seen that when placed so that they cut the planking more or less at right angles all along the hull, they show in effect the general 'run' of the planking.

In building they also enable a builder to check the outer edge curve of each of his moulds with added accuracy and the middle one, Diagonal B in this case, will give him approximately the position for his bilge stringer. For reading the design the diagonals are a fair indication of the fore and aft, or longitudinal, form of the hull, and the practised eye can pick out the irregularities in their sweeping curves which tell of a possibly unwelcome hollow or fullness in the hull. When it is remembered that as the yacht heels when sailing the diagonals represent graphically the actual path taken by the water along, or rather, beneath the hull, the importance of 'sweeping' diagonals which are free from ''umps and 'ollers' will be appreciated.

That completes the lines of the hull so far as the builder is concerned : given the sheer plan, sections, waterlines, buttocks and diagonals, he should be able to go ahead and build the hull accurately. To assist him the designer generally draws up in addition a table of offsets, in which he gives the exact spacing of these lines from the base lines. With his finer rule he is generally able to scale these off more accurately than the builder, who may work only with a two-foot rule and a boat builder's pencil with a lead the thickness of one's little finger. This offset table gives the exact length of the ordinates at all stations of the height above LWL at the deck edge, the depth below LWL of the keel profile, the 'half breadths' or distances of the deck edge from the centreline of the keel, and the 'half breadths' of all other waterlines and diagonals at each station. All these ordinates are employed for drawing and checking the lines when they are laid out full size on the mould loft floor. Incidentally by means of a complete table of offsets it should be possible to reproduce the complete design with fair accuracy without seeing the plan, provided the measurements have been scaled up from the plan with true accuracy.

With various other curves with which the designer can play, such as the Displacement or Half-Section Areas curve, the curve of heeled areas and (I felt this was coming) the Metacentric Shelf curve, we need not concern ourselves here. They form checks or governing qualities on the completed design and are fully explained in articles on 'How to Design a Yacht' or in Norman L. Skene's standard text book *Elements of Yacht Design* (John Lane, 21s.) or again in that very excellent and practical treatise on how a designer sets about planning a yacht *Yacht Designing and Planning* by Howard I. Chapelle (Putnam, 15s.).

I am often asked to explain what is meant by such terms as 'full' or 'fine' waterlines, 'firm', 'weak' or 'hard' midship sections, what is indicated when a boat is said to have 'well balanced ends,' a 'bold sheer,' a 'full bow,' 'ample freeboard' or a 'fine run aft.' Unfortunately all such terms are entirely relative. Their meaning depends on a number of conditions as the *type* of boat, what she is intended for, her general dimensions, and so on. What would be an excessively full bow for a 30-ton cutter would be none too full for a 3-tonner :

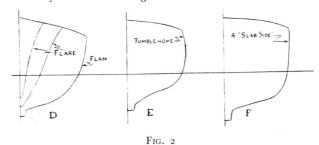

FIG. 2

a midship section that would be eminently suitable for a 25-ton ocean racer would be hopelessly weak for a 6-ton cruiser. In another sphere, to illustrate an example, what would appear in a Turk's eyes as a distressingly thin addition to the harem would, in London or New York, cause her friends to urge a course of slimming. As in women, so in boats, the fullness or flatness of curves depends on locality and purpose and their relative importance is acquired only by a trained eye and by the constant studying of all classes of yacht designs and of the completed boats themselves. Such terms, however, as flare, flam, tumblehome and wall- or slabsidedness are easily shown in Fig. 2, D, E and F respectively.

As each line in a design is shown from three different angles and all are closely interconnected, it is almost impossible to alter the curve of, let us say, one of the waterlines without affecting every other line throughout the ship. The design is like a complicated three dimensioned spider's web : if you pull one part of it, all the other parts are moved in ratio. Thus, a flaring bow, or forward sections having a tendency to flare or curve outward as they rise to the deck, results in completely different waterlines above the LWL and more drawn out buttock lines. The effect of the vertical cuts along the hull which we know as the buttock lines is to make them also hollow, but the hollowness is intensified, as shadows would appear along the curved surface of this hull when slanted by the setting sun. Fig. 3 (G) is drawn to show the relative shape of the buttocks A and B in the bow of a boat with hollow, flaring sections, and below (Fig. 3, H) as the same buttocks would appear in a bow with full round sections. To a practised eye, the buttocks in each case would denote the *kind* of sections there are in the bow even if the half-body plan on the left were not shown. If, on the other hand, the topsides swelled out above the waterline and then fell in towards the deck, so that the beam at the deck was an inch or two less than it was, say, a foot below, this 'tumblehome' would produce quite a different buttock line. The end of the buttock would curve back on itself as it reached the deck, and the amount of tumblehome can be measured after some experience and training with the eye by the shape and suddenness of this backward curve in the buttocks.

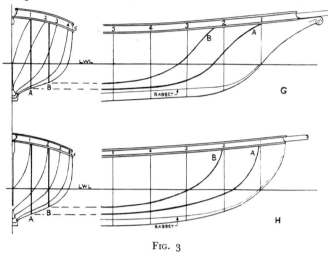

FIG. 3

The shape of the buttock lines from amidships aft reveal what used to be known as the 'run' of the ship, the passage the water takes when it rises from beneath the hull. Buttock lines that take a sudden turn up after passing through the midship section indicate a 'short' run. This means that the water will boil up as the short stern passes over it, sucking at the hull and dragging the ship back, so that she will be no fleetfoot. On the other hand, buttocks that stretch aft as almost straight lines indicate a 'long' or sweet run, allowing the water time to run up of its own accord without unnecessary suction on the hull, are productive of easy sections aft and a good turn of speed. But like all good things they must not be overdone, otherwise you have too fine a run and a ship that *would* go fast but lacks buoyancy or 'bearing' aft to carry her canvas to drive her fast.

Once these general principles of the lines of a ship are grasped and some idea gained of their importance and relationship one to the other, it is solely a matter of constant practice and the study of all sorts of designs for one to become at least familiar with the chief points in a yacht design and be able to see from the plans whether a yacht will be bluff bowed or fine, hollow in the run aft or full, high of side or lacking in freeboard, straight of sheer or comely, slab sided or gracefully flaring, an ugly box of a boat or a shapely ship. And then, not only the *appearance* should be visualized from a set of lines, but the probable behaviour of such a boat understood. In this connexion, it is as well for the student at first to confine his study to designs of yachts of approximately the same size, until he feels himself entirely familiar with boats of that tonnage. Later on he will be able to appreciate the essential difference between the lines of a good 30-tonner and the lines of a good 10-tonner, and how a design for the one, however successful, scaled down to the other, or vice versa, is almost bound to create a failure. Which brings me to a little discussion on this thoroughly insular word ' tonnage.'

One of the many fascinating interests in yachting is the wealth of tradition that lies behind it. Take, for example, the question of tonnage. The English have a habit of referring to their yachts by an antiquated measurement known as the Thames, or Yacht Measurement, and because custom and usage die hard in England, this form of describing the approximate size of any yacht is still generally used in England. But elsewhere in the world yachtsmen speak only of the overall length, to describe, say, a 35-ft. cutter that an English yachtsman would call a ' 10-tonner.'

Yet I would not have it otherwise. Although the Thames Measurement is admittedly an antiquated method of designating a yacht, and only confusing to anyone outside the British Isles, it is akin to the beating of the bounds, the ceremony of the City of London keys, the distributing of Maundy money, tossing the pancake, and other quaint customs that mark the English as a race of individualists who honour their ancestors and wait for hours just to watch a pageant.

Attempts have been made from time to time to change this Thames Measurement habit, but without success : just as attempts are continually being made to get the British to give up their absurdly complicated coinage and measurements and to adopt the metric system—dollars and 2,000 lb. tons of course—but with equal lack of success. The old bulldog's collar may be shabby and too tight, but 'e don't want a better one !

The Humber Keel has not changed for centuries.

There is too much tradition behind the T. M. tonnage of yachts to be thrown away lightly. The very word, originally ' tunnage,' came into use for the first time in the English language in the fourteenth century, for in 1347 King Edward III levied a tax of three shillings on every 'tun' of wine imported. Somehow I like to think of a custom of present day yacht measurement that originated with those bluff, barrel-like little merchant ships with their single squaresails, that brought the rich red wine of Oporto across the stormy Bay of Biscay up the Channel to the port of Southampton or Winchelsea or Rye in those far-off days of the Middle Ages. There is a wealth of mellowed tradition in the use of ' tunnage ' that no amount of money could buy, and the measurement of ships and finally of yachts has a history of its own.

43

As the round bellied merchantmen of the fourteenth century were all very much alike in shape and proportion, some merely being larger than others, the capacity for tuns of wine was chosen as a very good and easy measurement. The tun was a large cask of 40 cubic feet capacity or roughly 250 gallons, and the general dimensions of a ship could be quickly reckoned when her 'tunnage' was known. In addition to those of the ancient wine trade with Portugal, the ships of other trades soon came to be measured for the levy of dues (for the English learnt their flair for taxation very early), and we find that in 1422, in the reign of King Henry VII, a law was passed that 'Keels that carry coals at Newcastle shall be measured and marked.' And in passing, I do not suppose those 'keels' referred to in the Act differed very materially from the simple, flat bottomed, bluff, double-ended keels, rigged with a single mast and a squaresail, that ply the Yorkshire rivers today.

By the middle of the sixteenth century ships were measured in cubic feet of capacity given by the simple formula :

$$\frac{L \times B \times D}{94} = \text{tunnage}$$

In this L was the 'tread of keel' or the length of the keel that touched the ground when the vessel was high and dry ; B was the breadth inside the ceiling (or the maximum width of the hold) and D was the depth of the hold. The arbitrary denomination 94 was originally arrived at to give a figure as near as possible to the majority of vessels' tunnages at that time.

In 1720 the formula was altered, the L and B being measured as before, but the D being taken as 'half the breadth', as it usually was in vessels of that time. This obviated the difficult task of measuring the depth of the hold of a vessel loaded. This formula of 1720, then, became :

$$\frac{L \times B \times \frac{1}{2}B}{94} = \text{tonnage}$$

The effect of this rule which assumed the hold depth to be but half the breadth at once appeared : build your ships narrower and deeper and you get greater capacity with much smaller 'tonnage' for dues. And the repercussions of this simple but somewhat stupid rule have been felt right down to this day.

This question of how to fix D, or the depth of hold of a merchant ship, for tonnage was a very vexed one. If you made it too arbitrary builders got around it by building deeper and narrower ships that were bad boats, or by some other way. In the national way of handling difficult problems the obvious solution presented itself : the depth was just ignored, and in 1773 what came to be known as the Builders' Old Measurement was introduced :

$$\frac{L - 3/5B \times B \times \frac{1}{2}B}{94} = \text{tonnage}$$

In this L was the 'length along the rabbet of keel' (from the forepart of stem under the bowsprit to the after part of the stern post at the keel), while B was the beam *outside* the planking but excluding rubbing strakes, etc. The deduction of three-fifths of the beam from the length (L) was calculated to allow for a raking stem.

Builders of racing yachts very quickly seized on the weakness in this formula—the exact measurement of the length—and reduced the rateable tonnage of their yachts by raking the stern post excessively or by setting it well inboard from the after end of the waterline. To prevent this practice from creating impossible 'rule cheaters' in 1854 the Royal London Yacht

Club and the Royal Mersey agreed to measure the length *on deck* from the fore part of the stem to the after part of the stern post—the 'length between perpendiculars' or LBP as we know it now. A year later, in 1855, the Royal Thames Yacht Club adopted the same LBP measurement, but increased the deduction for 'rake' from three-fifths to the full beam. The resulting formula, or 'Thames Yacht (Club) Measurement' is as in use today, namely

$$\text{T.M.} = \frac{(L-B)\,B \times \frac{1}{2}B}{94}$$

Thus the Thames Measurement of a yacht 32 ft. LBP and 12 ft. beam is calculated :

$$\frac{(32-12)\,12 \times 6}{94} \text{ or } 15\frac{32}{94} \text{ tons,}$$

and by our English yachtsmen she would be referred to as a '15-tonner.'

This tonnage by which the English yachtsman speaks of his yacht is not such a far cry from the early fourteenth century tunnage after all, is it? Although it ignores depth of hull, draught, fullness or fineness of body or ends, displacement, freeboard, overhang aft or sail area, and takes no consideration of overhang forward, it is in actual practice a very fair way of giving an idea of a yacht's general size. It is true that a '10-tonner' 30 ft. LBP by 10 ft. beam might be a skimming dish 42 ft. OA, 22 ft. LWL and but 18 in. draught, or a heavy displacement hooker of the 'all boat' kind, 30 ft. OA, 30 ft. WL and 7 ft. draught. She would still be '10 tons T.M.' But then would any better idea of the relative 'sizes' of these two extreme cases be revealed by the simple references to them respectively as a 30-footer and a 42-footer?

This T.M. tonnage is *not* the vessel's total weight or displacement, although with the old time ships for which it was planned the resulting figure was not far out. Nowadays the displacement of the yacht has no connexion with her T.M. tonnage and is a separate figure calculated for his own purpose by her designer.

For the payment of dock and light dues, in addition, a third tonnage figure is used. This is obtained by Lloyds' surveyor when the yacht is measured for registration purposes. The total internal capacity in cubic feet of the hull is calculated and the result, divided by 100, is called the 'Gross Tonnage.' From this certain allowances are deducted for space occupied for navigating and propelling the ship such as 'certified chart room,' Bosun's stores, engine-room, crew's quarters and so on ; the result is termed the 'Nett Register Tonnage' and is the figure on which all dues are levied.

A British registered yacht therefore has four different figures of tonnage—T.M., Gross, Nett Register, and Displacement.

VI

Going to a Builder; and the Specification

LIKE writing one's first book, building one's first boat is always a serious undertaking. In both cases there appear to be so much planning to be done beforehand, so many points to be decided, so many weeks or months of slow, laborious growth when it looks as though the work will never be finished, and finally so much possibility that when all is done the result will fall below expectation—will be, in fact, a failure—that you feel like a plaintiff in litigation who wishes he had never set the wheels of the law in motion.

When you build your second ship, most of the early problems are already settled, and when it comes to your fourth or tenth ship, why, you just put the matter in the hands of a capable naval architect, and don't bother any more about her until she is almost ready to launch. I am told by parents—for of this I have no experience at all—that it is the same with your first-born : and by the time the sixth puts in an appearance, you haven't any pride, enthusiasm or income left. That seems too bad to me, but I suppose there are other compensations.

Before I designed *Wild Lone II*—35 ft. 8 in. Bermudian yawl with 4 ft. 9 in. draught—for myself and had her built, I had had a good deal of supervision work to do for the building of other boats, and as *Wild Lone II* was largely a development of previous keel-boat designs which I had prepared for clients, nearly all the problems and details had already been worked out and put to the test.

One needs to watch a yacht being planned and built, step by step, to realize the number of difficulties that can arise and the number of details that can go wrong or at least prove disappointing. That is why it is generally so unwise for a beginner to have a boat built to his own plans without consulting a competent architect, or better still, owning one or two different boats. There is much more in quite a small cruising yacht or motor cruiser than the beginner ever dreams of, and without the knowledge that the experienced professional designer has gathered from years of close association with just such work, the novice is almost bound to make expensive mistakes which may—and in many sad cases do—cause his new dreamship to be a great disappointment.

If the owner-to-be has a pretty clear idea in his mind as to what his new ship is to be like probably the first consideration or limit to his dream is the matter of cost. In yachting, as in most things, you get just what you pay for, no more and no less. (This does not, however, repudiate the fact that many of the best things in life cost nothing at all.) If you are determined to have a very smart yacht indeed, with carefully laid white pine decks, with planking, covering boards, king plank, rail capping and deck fittings of well-finished teak, and her interior beautifully fitted up with careful cabinet work in choice woods, then you will have to pay a price in accordance with such first-class yacht finish ; and to maintain the ship in a condition suited to such a high standard you will have to pay accordingly. First-class yachting can be an expensive hobby.

46

On the other hand, if you are content to own a vessel like a smack almost devoid of teak, with painted coachroof, coamings, hatches and rail, and a plain matchboard fitted cabin, then she will probably be built at one half or even a third of the cost of the other ; but in every detail the workmanship will be of a lower standard and the general finish homely but rough. Whether you can be content with this standard of 'yachting' depends on your temperament.

Now it is quite useless approaching one of the good class yards on the south coast of England, the Clyde, or Long Island Sound, whose reputation and business have both been built up on their high standard of construction, and ask them to build your boat as roughly and cheaply as possible. They would either quote you for building to your plans to *their* usual high class specification—at a figure probably four times as much as you thought of—or refuse to touch the job. No good class yard will do 'cheap' work which would only become a monument to disgrace their reputation.

It is as necessary to choose the yard to build your boat as it is to choose your tailor to suit both your style and your pocket. Many an owner has been disappointed in the way his ship has been built, disgusted with the abnormal time taken or dissatisfied with an unexpectedly heavy bill for 'extras', through going to a yard unaccustomed to such work. I knew of one case where an inexperienced owner was attracted by a low quotation from a yard which normally built barges and lighters : as the building proceeded with many interruptions, mistakes and necessary alterations, he began to suspect his unwisdom and was assured of it when finally presented with an additional bill for 'extras' which was considerably more than the original quotation for the complete yacht !

The question of where to build is one which I have been asked most frequently by puzzled amateurs. It is the business of the naval architect to know the yards personally, which yards would be the most satisfactory for the particular building job in hand. It does not always follow, because Messrs. So and So have very fine yachts laid up on their 'ways during the winter and have built several splendid yachts in recent years, that they would be equally successful in building a 30-ft. centreboard yawl. Unless a yard has been accustomed to, and their men already trained in, building yachts of *approximately* the size required, the job would assume the nature of a guess in building, or a tentative experiment. It is only a first-class yard with many years' experience in almost all tonnages, such as Camper & Nicholsons, J. Samuel Whites, Fifes, Herreshoffs or Nevins, that can build a 25-footer with the same accuracy, finish and general high standard as one of their very large yachts. Only a few yards have the facilities, the experience and the suitably trained men (in the drawing office as well as the building shed and the foundry) to produce successful yachts of all sizes.

What kind and quality of work they are capable of is not the only thing the naval architect should know about the various builders : he should also be well acquainted with their respective methods both in building and in business. By knowing from previous experience just where any particular builder needs watching, or a firm hand, and where he can be left to do the work in his own way, the architect-surveyor can save the owner endless worry and probably a lot of money.

Each builder seems to have his own idiosyncrasies or faults ; but when you know them and how to circumvent these obstacles, the work goes smoothly forward. As a class yacht builders are honest people who have to work long and hard—I know few trades where the hours are so long, the work so heavy, and the return so small in proportion as the small boatbuilder's— and the owner is wise to use discretion and forbearance in dealing with his builder.

In little points almost every builder seems to have his weakness or obstinacy. One builder I know has a curious dislike of fitting stopwaters (soft wood plugs driven through a keel or stem scarph which swell when wet and stop the water from seeping up through the scarph into the ship) ; another buys a very poor brand of opening portlights unless warned in time ; another will fit his planking butts over a frame and perhaps arrange for two or more butts to be fastened to the same frame unless the owner insists on the point in his contract. The owner will have to find a way of dealing with such situations each time he goes down to see how the work is progressing, and should learn how to handle the builder when he says : ' Well, we always do it that way.' They are the minor crises that help to make building a yacht such—er —fun.

When you know your builder and can rely on him to build you exactly what you want, only quite a brief specification may be necessary. I have known thoroughly satisfactory cruising yachts built to no more detailed instructions than a rough sketch on a pocket-book leaf and a few notes on the back of an envelope. It would be feasible, I imagine, to have a ' J ' Class yacht built to even fewer details, but personally I shall not try it.

In the majority of cases it is wiser to supply the builder with a complete and detailed specification for him to work out his estimate. Unless every single item is specified to begin with before the contract is signed, every addition or alteration made by the owner or his representative afterwards is liable to be treated as an ' extra ' and charged accordingly. At the least, some confusion and maybe bad feeling will probably result.

As in these days of competitive building, particularly with the small, low priced yachts, the builder runs his estimate as near the bone as he dare, it is hardly fair to expect him to ' understand ' later on that, for instance, six brass opening portlights, not shown on the plans or mentioned before, should of course be included as ' part of the ship, you know.' Those six ports would probably cost the builder, even with trade discount, six pounds or so.

It is perhaps in the avoidance of this vexed question of ' extras ' and of mistakes which may call for expensive alterations and more delays during construction that the professional architect-surveyor can prove of the greatest benefit to the owner. The drawings and the specification from which the builder makes out his estimates and to which the yacht is eventually built, should be so comprehensive, within reason, that nothing but minor queries, which do not affect the cost of construction, should ordinarily arise during the building. Such a specification is not easily worked out, and its completion calls for a wide experience of building—and not only building, but of sailing in and generally owning—boats of the size and type to be built. However clear and well executed his own design may be, the novice nearly always falls short on his specification.

No yacht has ever been launched which could not be improved in some way or another— although I do know several owners so unimaginative as to believe their own ships to be beyond improvement. Every yacht that one designs and builds shows up certain faults, and by eliminating these (and, alas ! inadvertently introducing others) one gradually improves and improves until at least a thoroughly sensible and satisfactory ship may result, even if perfection, thank heaven, is unattainable.

The following is a specification which I had worked out over a number of years and applied to my own 10-tonner *Wild Lone II*. It is given here only as a specimen and could, of course, be altered, abbreviated, amplified or generally improved as circumstances required. In the building of my own boat and her sister ship *Jorrocks II* (for which some of the items had to be altered) this specification proved sufficient and no misunderstandings or unexpected 'extras' arose from beginning to end. Indeed, after *Wild Lone II* had been built to the following specification, the bill for 'extras and alterations' apart from the contract price totalled less than £7.

If some of the items appear sketchy it should be remembered that where possible I always like to show the items clearly *on the plans*, with or without a printed description alongside. Many builders, one finds, look at the long specification before quoting, and then fold it up and leave it in a drawer while they go ahead building to the plans. Most of them have a curious dislike of referring constantly to a long specification, but will keep the ship's plans pinned on a board always before them. The specification, however, is necessary to avoid conflict over small details.

SPECIFICATION

of a

10 TON AUXILIARY BERMUDIAN YAWL

LOA 35 ft. 8 in. LWL 28 ft. Beam 9 ft. 3 in. Draught 4 ft. 9 in.

1. GENERAL

The plans are the copyright of the Designer, only one yacht is to be built from them, and the plans are to be returned to the Designer after the yacht is taken over and accepted by the Owner.

The yacht to be built generally as shown on the plans, all measurements in the plans and table of offsets to be accurately followed, and no alterations to be made without the express wish and sanction of the Owner.

2. CONSTRUCTION

The yacht is to be strongly constructed in every way with a view to extended cruising under all weather conditions. The yacht must be built in a substantial shed in which she will be well protected from rain, wind and sun, and she is to be built under the supervision and to the satisfaction of her owner who will hold the right (1) to inspect the vessel at any time within normal working hours, and (2) to discard and have removed any material which in his opinion is not of sufficiently good quality to be used in the construction of this yacht.

3. MATERIALS

All wood to be of carefully selected quality, well seasoned, dry, free from sap, shakes and deteriorating knots. If the type of wood stipulated in the plans is unsuitable or difficult to obtain, suitable substitutes of equally good or better quality to be chosen to the Owner's satisfaction.

All iron work to be of best quality crown iron, heat galvanized after working. All other metal work to be of best quality to the satisfaction of the Owner.

4. CERTIFICATES

The Builders to arrange for the yacht to be surveyed and measured and certified for British registration by a Board of Trade representative and to have her registered number and net tonnage carved on her main beam as required by the registration.

5. IRON KEEL

To be cast to shape as on plans, weighing about 3½ tons, and to be bolted to wood keel with nine 1⅛ in. galv. steel bolts with large heads staggered alternately, the nuts to rest on washers in the centre of each oak floor.

6. BALLAST

Trimming ballast in cast lead pigs (about 5 cwt.) to be supplied by the builders and to be stowed to cause completed yacht to float at her designed waterline.

7. PLANKING

Selected close grained Pensacola pitch pine free from excess of knots. The planks to be sawn 1⅛ in. full, finished not less than 1 in. in long lengths, no plank with the exception of the garboards and adjacent strakes to be of greater width at any point than 5 in. nor less than 3½ in.

The planking to be through fastened with copper roove nails, two fastenings to be employed at each frame through each strake. The hooded ends to be truly fastened with brass screws well counter sunk, care being taken to prevent splitting of the strake ends.

8. FLOORS

Of English oak crook, moulded 4½ in. sided 4 in. at centre, spaced about 24 in. with arms (where possible) copper rove to bilge stringers. The fastenings to be well countersunk in planking and stopped.

9. BILGE STRINGERS

Pitch pine in one length from stem to stern, 4½ in. by 2 in. amidships tapering to 3½ in. by 1½ in. at ends as requisite. To be copper rove to frames, and ends of floors where the latter meet.

10. WOOD KEEL

Of English oak or selected elm, finished to shape as on plans, 7¼ in. moulded 21 in. sided at widest part, tapering as requisite and about 24 ft. in one length.

11. FRAMES

The hull to be substantially framed throughout as follows :

Steamed American elm frames, in one piece each side, to be finished not less than 1¼ in. by 1½ in., spaced 6 in. c.c. throughout, checked into keel and through fastened with copper rove fastenings.

12. STEM AND STERN POST

The stem to be in one piece of grown oak crook, moulded 6 in. sided 5 in. and shaped exactly as on plans, the chamfered edges to be flush and *parallel* to the plank ends. The stern post to be in one piece of English oak, moulded as on plan and sided 3½ in. at bottom and 3 in. top.

13. KNEES

Stern knees, apron and all deadwoods to be of sound English oak crooks, with the grain following the curve and through bolted with galv. iron bolts.

14. LODGING KNEES

Of $2\frac{1}{2}$ in. oak crook, through bolted, to be fitted in the way of the main mast beams (four) ends of the coaming, and mizen mast beam

15. HANGING KNEES

Two hanging knees of 2 in. oak crook to be fitted at both main mast beams and two more at one of the bridge deck beams

16. BREAST HOOK

To be of English oak crook, substantially through fastened to stem and beam shelves.

17. TIE RODS

Three yellow metal tie rods, $\frac{1}{2}$ in. diameter, to be fitted through main carlines alongside half beams at approximately 3 ft., 6 ft., and 9 ft., respectively, from after side of main mast beam ; heads to be of ample size and well recessed into planking and carlines.

18. BEAM SHELVES

Pitch pine 5 in. by $1\frac{3}{4}$ in. in one length, taking beam ends half dovetailed.

19. PIN RAILS

A strong galvanized iron or oak rail with two large size pins to be placed each side of foot of main mast and substantially bolted to main mast beam.

A swelling $2\frac{1}{2}$ in. by 20 in. with 3 pins also to be bolted to the rail capping each side of mizen mast between the shrouds.

20. CLEATS, FAIR-LEADS, ETC.

All cleats to be of teak and to be placed where necessary and convenient ; each one to have two through fastenings, and to be set at an angle of about 20° up towards the lead of the rope. Foresail (after) cleats to be 2 in. lower than jib sheet cleats on cockpit coamings to lead sheets clear of latter. Four cleats to be riveted to the rail timbers on each side at suitable points.

A towing bollard of oak, $3\frac{3}{4}$ in. by $3\frac{3}{4}$ in. and 9 in. above deck to be stepped in the horn timber aft and to take the heel of the mizen bumkin.

Jibsheet and other sheet fairleads to be *large* size lignum vitae through bolted, and placed where necessary.

21. TILLER

To be of high quality oak or ash, cut to shape with *spherical* hand end ; well bolted to rudder head cap. The tiller to be about 6 in. above the after coaming of well.

22. PORTLIGHTS

(1) Four opening brass portlights with 5 in. clear glass openings to be fitted in the coamings each side as shown.

(2) Two opening ditto with 4 in. glass openings to be fitted in fore coaming. A small inverted brass drawpull to be screwed at the lower rim of all portlights.

(3) Three circular decklights, 6 in. glass, to be fitted in coachroof as shown.

23. COAMINGS

To be of teak, $1\frac{1}{8}$ in. shaped as on plans.

24. COCKPIT

The cockpit to be self emptying through two drain pipes 1¼ in. diameter at fore end, leading at an angle aft through the ship's skin. The floor to slope down forward at an angle of 1 in 20, to be caulked and payed and the sides to be watertight as far up as the engine controls. The capping on the coamings to be flush inside, and a teak pin rack with belaying pin for fixing tiller to be fitted outside after coaming and under tiller. A teak seat for sailing to be fitted to each coaming as shown in way of tiller.

25. VENTILATORS

A mushroom ventilator with 4 in. shaft to be fitted as shown on plans over the galley.

26. DECKS

To be 1½ in. pine, substantially laid and covered with 12 oz. canvas, painted light stone colour. The canvas to be turned down over covering board and covered by half round rubbing piece ; and turned up at coamings and well covered by quarter round beading which must be thoroughly set in Jeffries' SEAMFLEX and well screwed to the coamings.

27. CABIN TOP

To be covered with 10 oz. canvas and painted. A teak hand rail to be extended as shown along each side. Hand rail to be quite plain in design to facilitate scraping and varnishing.

Painted pine chocks to be fitted to take dinghy as shown, and lashing eyes to be fitted for dinghy lashings.

28. MAIN HATCH

To be of teak with painted top and to have four ports of heavy gauge glass as shown. Cabin doors to open outwards and to have brass lock and key.

29. FOREHATCH

To be of M. G. 'double-coaming' pattern, of teak as on plans, the cover to be hinged with all-brass hinges and to have a rectangular deck light in centre, coamings to be 7½ in. high at afterend.

30. DINGHY

To be about 8 ft. 6 in. long, specially lightly built to haul aboard and to fit bottom upwards over centre of cabin top on chocks as shown. A canvas covered coir or cork fender to be fitted round gunwale.

31 GEAR & FITTINGS

The Builders to supply :

A teak folding table of pattern indicated with chocks on underneath side to fit over two brass pillar legs. Legs to drop and fit into chocks let flush into the floor (sole).

Light boards, fitted to main rigging.

2 galv. iron single boom crutches of type indicated, to fit into sockets suitably placed.

Deck mop.

Boathook.

Brass foghorn of approved pattern.

5 lb. lead and 10 fathoms marked sounding line.

One pair of good galvanized iron side lamps with 4½ in. plain lenses and draught proof cone burners.

One galvanized riding lamp.

Two paraffin lamps in gimbals with shields for saloon and one ditto lamp and shield for fo'c'sle. Good quality blue linoleum (plain) for fo'c'sle floor.

32. BILGE PUMP

One good quality brass plunger deck pump with discharge through side, to be fitted so as to be workable from cockpit. Barrel not less than 3 in. Suction end to be easily accessible and to lie in a galv. iron perforated box 6 in. by 5 in. by 3 in.

33. COAL STOVE

To be a Smith & Wellstood's blue enamelled No. 1 model 'Jack Tar' or 'Mate' to be securely fixed over asbestos sheeting screwed to shelf 9 in. above floor in position indicated. Shelf to have 3 in. gunwale around. All woodwork within 15 in. of stove or stove pipe to be effectively protected by asbestos sheeting. Flue to pass through cabin top by means of a Smith & Wellstood 'well deck' iron. Flue to be of asbestos pipe and chimney of *galvanized* iron piping.

34. WATER CLOSET

To be a Blake's 'Baby' (Bow model) w.c., efficiently installed in fo'c'sle, all plumbing fittings to be carefully made to prevent leaks.

35. ENGINE INSTALLATION

(Make and model of engine specified here). Builders to install engine and supply and fit tanks, etc. Every care to be taken to ensure a good, sound, solid job. The bearers to be of English oak sided not less than 2 in., through bolted securely to transverse bearers and carried as far forward and aft as practicable. A copper, brass or galvanized iron tray to be fitted under the engine and gear box, and a separate and easily removable copper tray, gauze covered, under the carburettor. Exhaust line to go up to deck near engine and lead out through counter at least 12 in. above LWL. Engine and shaft to be lined up after launching to owner's satisfaction.

36. TANKS

(1) A galv. iron F.W. tank to be installed as indicated with filler on deck. An 8-in. manhole to be in front end of tank, easily accessible while in place, and the tank to have at least four effective baffles. Lead pipe line to lead to water pump over sink in galley and to have cock at base of tank.

(2) A petrol tank (baffled) to be made entirely of copper sheet and strengthened as necessary, to be securely installed with straps where shown.

37. GROUND GEAR

One 56 lb. bower anchor, fisherman type, one 35 lb. C.Q.R. as spare and one 36 lb. kedge. 35 fath. of best calibrated short link $\frac{3}{8}$ in. chain cable and 30 fath 2$\frac{1}{2}$ in. warp. Windlass of approved pattern with gypsy wheel to fit cable to be solidly fitted where necessary.

38. STANDING & RUNNING RIGGING

Sizes and types as shown on plans. No blocks to be smaller than 3$\frac{1}{2}$ in. shell. All main blocks to be 4$\frac{1}{2}$ in. (Blocks and halyards stipulated on Sail Plan).

39. SAILS

Of good cotton canvas and of approximate weight shown. To be mildew proofed or dressed. Sails, etc. to consist of :

   (1) Mainsail, to have one row of reefing eyelets with luff and leech cringles at the third reef.

   (2) Mizen, to have one row of reef pendants and cringles.

   (3) Trysail, to have large cringles for lacing toggles on the luff, and one deep reef with large size reef pendants.

   (4) Foresail, to have one row of reef pendants and cringles.

   (5) Working jib.

   (6) Storm jib.

   (7) Jib topsail, to set on hanks.

   (8) Mizen staysail.

   (9) Canvas tiers for main and mizen.

   (10) Canvas dinghy lashings and lanyards.

40. ROLLER REEFING

The main boom to be fitted with worm roller gear for 4 in. boom. The gooseneck to be arranged to fit the double band fitting on mast. (The mizen boom to have chock for single reef tackle at after end.)

41. MAST FITTINGS

Main mast tack to be of internal slide C-section type, of heavy brass, with brass slides and shackles. Mizen mast track to be of similar type in brass with slides of size smaller.

Crosstrees to be of ash and shaped as indicated on main mast, bolted to mast irons as shown.

42. SPARS

   (1) Mainmast, circular $6\frac{3}{4}$ in. at deck tapering as requisite, of solid spruce.

   (2) Mizen mast $4\frac{3}{4}$ in. of solid spruce.

Each to have built-out ridge piece at after side as shown at lower end to lead sail track out requisite amount. Masts to be raked aft as shown and chain plates to be carefully located as on plans.

   (3) Main boom, of length indicated, 4 in. diameter at after end, $3\frac{3}{4}$ in. at fore end ; to have wood lacing track whole length.

   (4) Mizen boom, 3 in. diameter and length as shown with sheave for leech reef tackle.

   (5) Bowsprit 5 in. at heel. A straight grained pitch or oregon pine spar. To have rounded end to project about 3 in. beyond crans iron.

   (6) Mizen bumkin, $3\frac{1}{2}$ in. ash, grown to shape of curve as shown, and stepped in towing bollard. To be strong enough not to need stays.

43. IRONWORK

   (1) Bobstay to be $\frac{3}{8}$ in. G.I. bar, set taut. To have 30 in. of 1 in stout hose pipe threaded over as chain silencer.

   (2) Bowsprit chain fairlead, with 3 in. diameter roller on one side as shown.

   (3) Chain lead at stem head to have two leads and rollers, rollers to be large size (3 in. dia.) Lugs to be turned inwards at the top.

   (4) Mainmast gooseneck to have two G.I. bands, 9 in. apart, lower band to have 2 belaying pins

(5) Mizen mast gooseneck to be standard fitting with spider band and belaying pins.

(6) Windlass to be through bolted where necessary.

(7) Rudder stock to work in 2½ in. G.I. tube securely fastened at deck and horn timber. Rudder stock to be G.I. and shaped as shown, to rest on heel of keel as on plan.

(8) Staysail horse of ⅝ in. dia. galv. iron bar, placed as necessary 2 in. above deck, about 4 ft. long, bolted through one deck beam.

(9) 2 galv. iron boom crutches for main and mizen to fit in deck slots as shown.

44. INTERIOR WOODWORK

(FO'C'SLE). Sides to be lined flush to within 3 in. of beam shelves from after bulkhead to abreast samson post.

Lining to be gloss painted cream.

Seats and locker tops to be left varnished.

Blake's ' Baby ' w.c. to be hidden under hinged cover.

Bulkhead to galley to be varnished and have sliding door with at least 18 in. opening.

Floorboards of deal, lino. covered.

(GALLEY). Shelf for stoves to be asbestos lined and to have 3 in. rail around. Shelf for saucepans, etc. to be fitted above. Starboard side, sink not less than 15 in. by 9 in. to be fitted with seacock to drain pipe in accessible position. Fresh water pump, connected to F.W. tank, to be fitted near sink as shown. Plate racks and shelves to be made also as shown. Seawater inlet, with seacock, to be fitted beneath sink.

(SALOON). Chest of two drawers with locker beneath on port side ; sideboard with upper locker opening aft and lower opening athwartships to starboard. Book shelf in teak over.

Berth bottoms to be 10 in. above cabin sole (floor), to have 1½ in. hollow in the centre. Both berths to have shelf and lockers at back. Berth cushions to be Vi-spring or similar approved make of spring cushion, with waterproof permanent covers and loose outer covers of good quality blue rep.

Wardrobe to have bulkhead fore and aft at back, allowing a blanket locker to open out on to port berth with floor same level as top of berth mattresses.

Table to be of teak with two flaps, solidly fastened to floor on tubular brass legs.

Coal stove shelf to be lined with asbestos and to have 4 in. pine rail. Coal box to be fitted where possible, with shelf at back.

The saloon and galley floor boards to be of ⅞ in. teak, planed and oiled only. No lino. covering.

Companion steps of teak varnished. To fold down over engine as necessary.

Teak mouldings to be fitted to edges of all lockers, etc. where directed, and varnished. All other outside parts of lockers of pine, enamelled cream.

Bridge deck of pine, stone colour painted like lower part of cockpit and decks.

45. PAINTING

HULL to be thoroughly coated with ' Cuprinol ' (wood preservative) inside and painted light stone behind linings as yacht is built.

The cabin top to be painted light stone.

Decks to be painted light stone.

Coamings, hatches, tiller, rail cap, varnished.

Inside of rail, stone.

Timber heads, teak colour.

Topsides and rubbing piece enamelled cream (old ivory).

Boot top green.

Bottom treated with anti-fouling undercoating and finished green antifouling of brand to be specified by Owner.

INTERIOR. Ivory enamelled and teak varnished mouldings as indicated. Cabin sole (teak) to be oiled.

46. CLEANING

The interior of the yacht to be swept and cleaned of all shavings, sawdust, matches and rubbish, all corners and crannies to be swept clean of dust and all foreign matter liable to choke limber holes or bilge-pump to be removed before the vessel is handed over to the Owner.

47. OMISSIONS

Any item necessary for the safety or seaworthiness of this vessel omitted from this specification to be supplied by the Builder, and to be of the same standard of quality as the rest of the yacht.

Upon acceptance of the builder's quotation an agreement should be drawn up clearly stating the terms of the contract, so that there shall be no misunderstanding just what work he is to do, how much he is to be paid, and when the work should be completed and the vessel handed over (Queen Elizabeth once had 'must' altered to 'should' in an important state document. Being a woman she realized the true worth of agreements). How much of the contract price is paid on the signing of the agreement and how and when the balance is paid to the builder, is largely a matter of agreement between owner and builder. I have usually arranged for one third to be paid at the signing, one third when the yacht is planked, and the final third when she is *accepted* as complete by the owner after preliminary trials under power.

The following is the form of agreement which I have come to use and which, so far, appears to have met all needs. I do not suggest this as a watertight legal document : it is composed so that both the builder and the owner can understand it from beginning to end. A lawyer could draft out a much more imposing document, like a verbal obstacle race from WHEREAS to the end, but it would give me a headache to grasp all its complexities and I am sure the average builder would fold it up and put it away with a shake of the head.

SPECIMEN AGREEMENT WITH BUILDER

MEMORANDUM OF AGREEMENT made this   day of   19   between   (hereinafter called the Owner) and Messrs. J—— B——— & Son, The Shipyard, W———, in the county of H———, Yacht Builders (hereinafter called the Builders).

WHEREBY the Builders agree to construct and complete an auxiliary Bermudian yawl rigged yacht, 35 ft. 8 in. LOA, 28 ft. 0 in. LWL, 9 ft. 3 in. beam and 4 ft. 9 in. draught according to plans and specification drawn up by the Naval Architect. The workmanship and materials to be first class and to be of reasonable satisfaction to the Owner or his appointed Representative, whose decision in all matters in connexion with the construction of the yacht and materials used is to be final and binding. The yacht to be delivered to the Owner or his representative, complete according to plans and specification, with sufficient lead ballast stowed in a proper manner to trim her to her designed waterline, and with the bilges inside the hull clean and swept of all sawdust, shavings and foreign matter, after at least one

hour's satisfactory trial under the engine alone, safely moored off the Builder's yard not later than mid-day,   the first day of   19   IN CONSIDERATION WHEREOF the Builders shall be paid by the Owner the sum of   in full and complete payment, thus :
(1)   on the signing of this Agreement, the receipt of which the Builders herewith acknowledge, (2)   when the yacht is completely planked and decked, and (3)   when the yacht is launched and has been taken over by the Owner to his entire satisfaction. THE YACHT, after payment of the first instalment of   , on signing of this Agreement shall become the property of the Owner and all material intended for the building of the Yacht shall be deemed the property of the Owner.   If at any time the Builders shall become bankrupt or enter into any arrangement with their creditors under the Bankruptcy Act, or shall be unable to complete the said Yacht in accordance with this Agreement, or shall be guilty of any unreasonable delay in the execution of the work agreed to be done therein, then it shall be lawful for the Owner or his representative to take full possession of the Yacht in the Builders' yard, or where ever the said Yacht be placed, and to cause the work, as included in this Agreement, to be completed by any person or persons whom the Owner or his representative may appoint.   All damage that shall occur to the said Yacht during its course of construction and material intended to be used in its construction, by fire, floods or any cause whatsoever shall be made good by the Builders.   An Insurance Policy shall be taken out by the Builders in the joint names of the Builders and the Owner to such an amount as to fully cover the Builders against loss by fire or other causes under the previous clause.   The Builders shall not be entitled to make any claim or demand upon the owner for work done on the yacht or its equipment or for any alterations or extras beyond the contract sum, unless the order describing the extra work be given in writing by the Owner.   Any dispute arising between the Owner and the Builders respecting anything contained in the Agreement, the plans or specification, or in any way relating to the building of the Yacht or in its equipping or delivery, shall be referred to an arbitrator, to be agreed upon between the parties, the cost of any such reference to be to the discretion of the arbitrator.
IN WITNESS whereof the parties hereunder set their hands this   day of   in the year One Thousand Nine Hundred and

OWNER	....
ADDRESS	....
WITNESS	....
ADDRESS	....

It will be noticed that no ' penalty clause '—at so much per diem if the delivery date is exceeded—is included.   With the delivery of so many iron and metal fittings from various chandlers, and much else that may delay the work quite reasonably, I prefer to try to do without any such penalty clause in yacht building.   There has not been, I believe, a test case, but I am certain that no court, in normal circumstances, would uphold such a clause when yachts are only playthings and their delivery by a certain date not usually financially injurious to the owner. There is only one type of clause that I know of which can act much in the same way as a ' so much per diem' penalty clause, and is understood to be enforced at law, but I feel it has no place just here.

And now that the contract is signed, the plans, specification and all details completed and in the builder's hands and the deposit paid, we are all set to watch the building.

Come on, let's go.

VII

Building a Yacht

EVERY builder has his own methods, and as I said in the previous chapter, it is the duty of your architect-surveyor creature to know them and to look after your—the owner's—interests accordingly. Trying to induce the average small builder to build a boat in a way he is unaccustomed to is like trying to get a family lawyer to take a legal short cut.

At some yards the owner is not welcome and any suggestions he makes are treated like enquiries about mail at a rural post office. The yard have the job in hand, it is intimated, and the yacht will be ready on the appointed date ; there is surely nothing else he wants to know ?

At other yards the owner can have the run of the place, and some owners who have no jobs themselves to keep them away do prove to be perfect pests when the builder and his men are anxious to get on with their work. For, believe it or not, there is an immense amount of labour in the building of a yacht, just ordinary, hard labour. And the smaller the yard, the fewer the mechanical aids, and the harder the builder and his men have to work.

It is this labour that runs up the cost of building a yacht, and it should not be forgotten that if, in estimating the price of the job, the builder has underestimated the amount of labour involved, he is almost bound to lose on it. The longer the yacht remains in his shed with one or more of his men working on her, the higher will be his own costs and the less his profit—or the greater his loss, poor man.

That is why demanding a first-class finish on all work and high quality cabinet work below decks doubles or even trebles the cost of building to a ' cheap ' standard. This finishing-off work to a high degree takes a man a long time, all of which costs so much an hour. One man who is very capable with his tools built himself, with his own hands, a nice little 25 ft. sloop. Although he was retired and, except for family holidays away from home, spent *all* his time working on the ship, it took him *over three and a half years* to complete her for sailing. But then, he put a good finish on everything, and told me that, doing the work again, he would build much more roughly and probably take a third of the time.

Owners, therefore, who make a habit of calling the builder or any of his men from their work to discuss at interminable length some proposed alteration to the interior layout, or structural addition to the ship should not complain if this goes down in the account for ' extras '. It is an unhappy fact that most yachtsmen on visiting a yacht yard are just thirsting to button-hole someone and to yarn about boats until one or the other drops exhausted, and if they cannot find anyone else, they pounce on the hapless builder and expect him to down tools and discuss cheerfully with them everything they want to know. No wonder the builder usually tries to avoid the assaults of such people at week-ends, when he has been working long hours throughout the week at nothing but boats. I can sympathise with the two or three builders I know who

58

spend Sunday morning at the local chapel. I imagine it's about the only place to which these thirsting yarnswoppers won't track them.

Before any wood is cut the first thing that the builder must do is to lay down the yacht's lines *in full size* on a clear space. This is generally done in white chalk on the mould loft floor ; and not only the body plan (showing the various sections to the exact shape of which the moulds must be made) but the sheer plan (giving the exact profile of the stem, the keel and the sheer or deck line) also in full size is thus laid down. These lines are enlarged very carefully from the designer's own plans, and it will be seen that if there are any discrepancies in the latter the fault will be greatly magnified. Here is where a complete 'table of off-sets', giving the exact measurements of the various curves by ordinates in feet, inches and eighths, which should accompany the plans, comes in valuable as a check on the lines.

From these full-size plans the moulds—the temporary frame sections, built up of odd deals and scrap wood, round which the hull will be built—are cut and made up, templates or moulds of the stem and stern post are made and the chosen pieces of oak in due course cut to the shape of these moulds.

Before the lead or iron keel can be ordered the builder has to make an exact mould for it. This is a built up replica of the keel in wood, well trussed and strengthened inside so as to prevent warping when the moulding earth is rammed hard all around it. Because both lead and iron shrink after cooling, allowance must be made in making the keel mould so that when cooled and shrunk the keel is the exact size and form required by the plans. The keel mould, therefore, must be made a fraction larger than shown on the plans, and because of the accuracy and strength required for the purpose there is sometimes as much labour involved in making the keel mould as there is in a complete dinghy !

The builder is wise to order his iron keel first and not to drill the holes in his oak or elm keel for the keel bolts until the foundry has delivered the goods. Unless the shrinkage of the metal in cooling has been most accurately worked out, it is easy for the bolt holes not to register in both keels, and then, why he may be a chapel goer, but I guess the builder will say what's in his mind.

A week or two—sometimes several—elapse while the foundry is left to deliver the keel and nothing much else seems to be done in the yard. Actually, of course, unless he has the big timber stocks of a large yard on hand, the builder is visiting timber merchants, looking for a ' nice bit o' hoak, or hellum ' for the keel and the deadwoods.

In a centreboard yacht the keel is generally fairly wide amidships—one 12-tonner I saw building had an elm keel nearly 4 ft. wide at the top and about 24 ft. in length. Even *Wild Lone II*'s keel was finished 21 in. wide and 24 ft. long. Such a chunk as the centreboarder's needs a big tree from which it could be cut and it is not always easy to find an oak large enough, so that one is left with elm.

Some owners spend sleepless nights and absent-minded days puzzling over the relative suitability of oak and elm for their new boat's keel and details of that kind. I often feel sorry for their wives. It must be better, and freer, to be a golf widow than a party to nocturnal monologues on ' can't make up my mind, dear. You see, oak ought to be felled at the proper time of the year. . . .'

Provided the elm has been carefully chosen I do not see any really serious reason why it should not be accepted for a yacht's keel, when it is nearly always submerged. It is along the waterline—' between wind and water '—where elm is always liable to develop rot, and should not be used. Thus the stem, the stern post, and the planking (other than the garboards only) should not be of elm.

Many arguments have been spilled on the relative merits of lead and iron keels. On the question of cost the iron benefits, for at the time of writing an iron keel, cast and faired, at a British yard will cost about £6 a ton, while a lead one will be in the region of £28 a ton. Whether the extra cost of lead is worth it depends on the type of yacht to be built. Certain yards, where only first-class work is taken on, will not build a yacht with an iron keel, just as they would not build a yacht with canvased decks or painted pitch pine coamings. They have their well-earned reputation for the highest class *yacht* construction, and it is right that they should not try to meet the needs of an owner who does not want a first-class yacht.

Lead by its greater density (roughly lead : iron is as 11 : 7 ; or 700 lb. per cu. ft. : 440 lb. per cu. ft.) puts the centre of gravity lower, and the keel in consequence can be smaller and shorter. In a small *cruising* yacht I do not consider this a very important point. A lead keel is very liable to give trouble every few years with the corrosion and ' rotting ' of keel bolts, even when one believes just the right ingredients for the metal alloy have been used. Again, lead is a very soft metal, and is best kept in a big, short lump, as in a modern, deep-keeled boat. In a shoal draught cruiser the keel is usually both long and shallow, and if this is of lead and the yacht should pound badly on a hard bank, or hit a rock heavily with her keel, the lead can become wrung, setting up a tremendous strain on the hull ; and it will never be straightened out again. The slot for the centreboard is also liable to become burred at the edges if the keel is of lead, and I remember once examining the underside of a centreboard yacht's lead keel after she had slid over a stone breakwater. The lead in places was pressed up as though it might have been butter, and the edges of the slot were so jagged that they had jammed the centreplate.

An iron keel is a very strong backbone, in addition to the wood keel, on which to build the ship, and there is not the need to examine the keel bolts nearly so often as with a lead keel. The greater length of the iron keel, carrying some of its weight out towards the ends of the ship, will not allow her to be quite so lively as if she had a lead keel, but in most cruisers I consider this is, in fact, an advantage. As a tall mast slows up a yacht's rolling, so weights spread out in a hull have the effect of making most boats slower and steadier on their helm.

When the oak keel has been sawn and adzed to the shape shown on the plans, the slot cut in the centre to take the C.B. case, and along each side the ' rabbet '—the groove along which the inner edge of the garboard strakes will lie—has been cut and faired off, it is laid over and bolted on to the iron keel, which it should fit exactly, or be faired off until it does. The stem, the stern post and the oak or elm deadwoods that fill up the keel profile between the iron keel and the stern post, are now bolted into position together with the grown oak floors, which are really very heavy garboard frames and are made to bear the weight and straining of the keel and ballast.

The floors may be one of three or four kinds such as grown oak crooks, straight sawn elm or ash filling pieces, mild steel angle frames galvanized, or even of yellow metal. In small

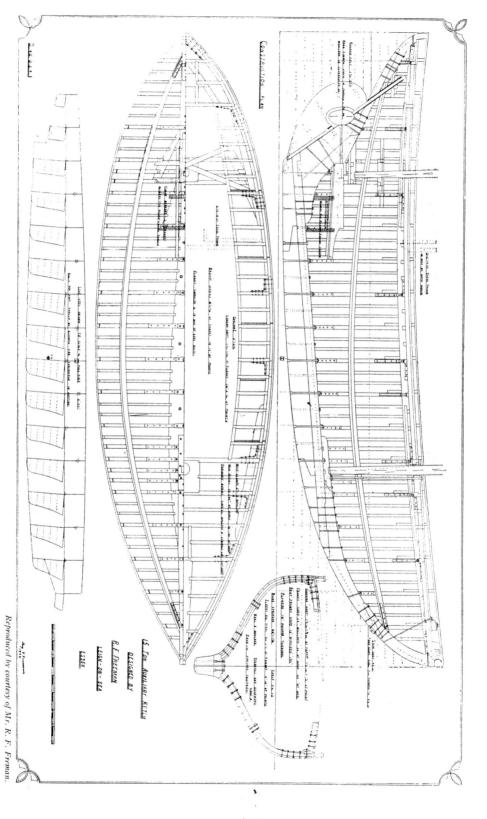

A typical construction plan for a 15-ton ketch of moderate draught showing sizes and arrangement of all frames, floors, beams, knees, carlines, stringers, shelves, engine bearers, keel, deadwoods and so on.

Reproduced by courtesy of Mr. R. F. Freeman.

vessels, say up to 40 ft., I have a preference for an all-wood construction, unless the extra *space* taken by heavy grown oak floors is needed. Galvanized iron or mild steel floors take up little room and allow the floorboards (or cabin sole) to be laid several inches lower, but the iron in time is almost bound to produce a dirty bilge and give the ship that indescribable 'boaty' smell. The all-wood ship with no iron floor straps or ballast will remain sweet smelling so long as engine oil, petrol and paraffin are kept out of the bilge. Yellow metal is too uncertain to be recommended. The term covers all qualities of yellow metal from ironmongers' brass to Naval

Stern view of *Vivette II*, 12 ton C.B. ketch (plans on Page 79), showing moulds and splines in place. The bow view shows garboard strakes being fastened on.

bronze, and unless the formula for making it has been rigidly adhered to its strength is a gamble. I am still a lover of good, clean, selected wood, and there is nothing better for a small yacht's floors and knees and other crooks that have to take a heavy strain than the best English oak.

Next, the moulds, each one carefully shaped to one of the sections measured to the *inside* of the planking, are erected over the top of the keel and spaced at the regular intervals set out on the plans. Like the stem and the stern posts, these moulds, for the time being, are usually held aloft by temporary pieces nailed to the shed rafters. Around these moulds several rough deal stringers or splines about 2 in. by 1 in. are run from end to end, just as the planking will run, and any discrepancies in the shape of the moulds will be revealed and corrected.

Now if the ship is to be framed throughout, or alternately, with grown oak frames (that is with oak selected with its grain following the average curve of the frame) sawn to the shape of the sections, these will be next fastened in place, their lower ends being checked (or countersunk) into slots cut in the keel and held with spikes. The planking will then be laid around these frames and duly fastened.

Whether steamed timbers are 'better' than grown frames, apart from their generally lower cost, is not decided. An all bent framed vessel has a more resilient, livelier hull and is usually in consequence faster, while such a hull, although prone to 'working' normally, is very tough and the frames are not given to breaking. On the other hand the sawn oak framed hull in theory should be stronger because of the amount of wood used, but it is very rigid, and not conducive to a sea-kindly ship nor a fast one. Again, the higher cost of sawing the frames

Vivette II nearly planked up, and (right) view of her centreboard case and grown frames, stringer and deck beams.

to the proper shape and the consequent wastage of timber cancels out the lower cost, say, of using galvanized iron spikes in place of copper rooves; and should the vessel ever be badly crushed between two barges in a dock, for example, the grown frames are almost bound to break whilst the bent frames usually spring back to shape.

It is possible, for those who must, to save considerably on the costs of building a small vessel by simplifying methods of construction. This is done in most fishing boats and work boats and not a few 'yachts' built at yards where fishing craft are normally built. The labour of checking the heel of every frame into the keel and the cost of cutting grown oak crooks, selected for their grain, which should follow the curve for the floors may be reduced by adopting 'workboat construction'. The ends of the frames are made to rest on top of the keel (in some weakly constructed boats I have inspected with steamed timbers, the timbers have ended on the garboards and have not even reached the keel. All working of the garboards and the weight of the keel are supposed to be taken care of by the floors) and are bolted to cross members which fulfil the dual purpose of floors and floorboards. Fig. 1 shows this simplified construction which in the United States and the Baltic countries, where hardwood is not always easy to get, is frequently carried out entirely in soft wood such as pine.

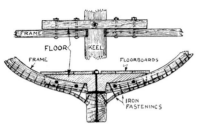

FIG. 1.—'Cheap' method of fastening the frames and floors to the keel in fishing boat construction.

This is neither a very strong nor sound form of hull construction, as the working strains of the hull which are always concentrated towards the garboards are controlled mainly by the fastenings joining the frames to the floor bearers. When these become weak, as they are bound to in time, the whole hull will begin to work and the garboard seams will become troublesome and leaky. Many old fishing craft and poorly built yachts give trouble in this way and one should not imagine that 'immense' frames and massive floors necessarily mean a strong and tight hull.

On the question of the best method of fastening the planking there has been great argument. I do not think there is any true finality about it, as in so many of these yachtsmen's opinions. Although galvanized iron fastenings have been known to last for fifty years and more, for a yacht whose owner does not wish to drop too much money when he sells it is a false economy to try to save on the slightly higher cost of copper or yellow metal fastenings. The spikes are too small to last very long once corrosion does set in and it is almost impossible to prevent, in due course, the appearance of rust marks down the topsides of an iron-fastened yacht. For use as a yacht any boat loses her value when it is found that she is iron fastened, even though iron spikes can be driven so hard into good oak frames that the hull may be much stronger and it is known that no yellow metal fastenings used in yachts can last as long as good quality iron ones. It just happens that iron fastenings for yachts have gone out of fashion and it does not pay to use them in new yachts.

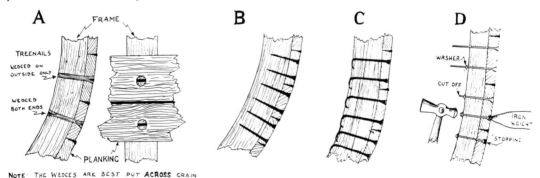

NOTE: THE WEDGES ARE BEST PUT ACROSS GRAIN

FIG. 2.—Four methods of fastening planking : (A) treenails (B) iron spikes (C) clenched spikes (D) copper roove (in process).

The various methods that have been adopted for fastening the planking to the frames are shown in Fig. 2. A is the old treenail (trennel) fastening no longer used for yachts, but still used for wood craft in many parts of the world and often to be found in smacks. A light wedge is generally driven flush into the outer end, set so as to open the treenail with the grain : and it is much better if the treenail passes right through the frame so that its inner end can be cut off flush and wedged similarly. It is an excellent form of fastening, since there can be no corrosion, and the treenails will last as long as the rest of the hull. But the surface along the planking cannot be kept quite so smooth as with countersunk and 'stopped' fastenings. *B* shows the ordinary iron spike fastening in a grown oak frame. Iron spikes can be driven very hard and usually hold like grim death, until they corrode away. And then, as the strength of a chain is that of its weakest link, so the strength of the hull becomes that of its rotting fastenings. Many an innocent yachtsman has saddled himself with an antique iron-fastened fishing craft, intending to convert her, and pointed with pride to the massive frames and knees and beams, only to learn in sorrowful sequence how the heaviest of frames can part company with the biggest of keels when the iron spikes joining them have become reduced to thin rusty shadows.

Some builders clench their fastenings, as shown in *C*, whether they are of iron, copper or yellow metal. It is not a good method, as the fastening is always 'started' by the hammer blows from inside the hull, and if the frame is a small steamed one, it usually becomes bruised and cracked in the way of the clenches. Also, if the fastenings are of iron, the galvanizing nearly always gets chipped off by the clenching and rust begins its fell work from the day the ship is built. It is just a cheap way of making the fastenings 'hold'.

The usual yacht practice with square sectioned copper nails 'roove' or riveted over round copper collars on the inside of the frame is shown, in its operations, in *D*. The nail is driven through a hole already drilled through planking and frame, the planking being countersunk to a depth of about $\frac{1}{4}$ in. to take the head of the fastening. These holes, incidentally, have to be the right size. If too small the soft copper nail will buckle and jib, for you cannot drive copper as you can an iron nail, and if it is too 'easy' the fastening will never be really firm and under years of strain and stress will 'work' throughout the ship. Not a pleasant thing to have a soft fastened ship.

A copper collar or washer is threaded over the end of the nail and the surplus length cut off. Then with a boy holding a heavy iron against the nail head to keep it from being driven out, the inner end is mushroomed or 'rooved' with a round-headed hammer, and the fastening is complete and forms a copper rivet.

In copper-fastened yachts that have iron floors or steel straps over the tops of the oak floors the problem of how to fasten these floors arises. If copper or yellow metal fastenings are used, the iron around the fastening corrodes away from the action of the salt moisture and bilge water which causes a strong galvanic action between iron and copper. On the other hand, if iron fastenings are used so as to agree with the floors, they strongly disagree with the copper fastenings on the *outside* of the planking. They may be 'stopped' with putty and linseed oil or some other special stopping, but, like love, the water will find a way, and corrosion of the iron begins. Yachtsmen I have met have spent sleepless nights thinking out a solution to this neat problem and in my search to get it O.K. (to misuse the poet's initials and his famous lines) I

    .... Did eagerly frequent
Builder and Designer, and heard great Argument
About it and a bout : But evermore
Came out by the same Door as in I went.

Accepted practice is to use copper or Y.M. fastenings, allow for ample strength in the iron floors so that some corrosion will not weaken them too much, and when corrosion has gone too far, to replace the iron floors. You can *see* how the floors are corroding inside the hull, and up to a point it does not much matter ; but you cannot see how iron fastenings are holding under their stopping outside the hull, and nail sickness is a far more serious complaint and not nearly so easy to rectify.

A point worth insisting upon, provided you are concerned with the eventual life of the ship you are building, is to have all timber faces, joints, dovetails and scarphs, painted—soused is a more appropriate word—with creosote or other good wood preservative before being fitted together. All frame heels where they will be checked into the keel, all plank ends, every bit of timber that has a cut face which will be inaccessible once it is in place. It certainly discourages eventual saturation and rot.

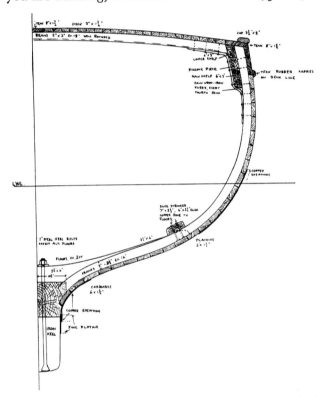

This midship half section, showing the scantlings of a 30-ton shoal draught keel cruiser (*Sunquest*, see page 133) explains the usual fitting of the keel, oak floors, bilge keels, shelves (two each side here because amidships the deck in this ship is raised to the height of the forward and aft bulwarks) and frames. The zinc strip covering the join between the iron and oak keels is there to absorb the galvanic action that will set up between the iron and the copper sheathing.

The ship is now fully planked up with frames, floors and keel in place. Nowadays we do not fit a keelson, or son of a keel, over the floors and carrying the keel bolts. The keelson used to be an important backbone of old yachts before wide and much bigger keels came in and the existing keels were merely narrow planks on edge. Some yachts' keelsons were of iron. It was really an easy method of fitting an iron keel, except that it was bolted to the tops of the oak floors instead of at the bottom of the wood keel.

A keelson took up a good deal of room, but in a deep hull with a sharp 'V' section there was plenty of space beneath the floorboards for 6 in. by 6 in. oak frames, 8 in. by 12 in. oak floors and maybe a 7 in. by 5 in. pitch pine keelson. Eighty years ago an English cutter yacht's hull compared with a modern cruiser's in material proportion as an earthenware bowl does with an enamel one.

The bilge stringers may next be put into place before any deck beams are fitted. Some builders fit the bilge stringers when the hull is 'in frame', that is when all the floors and frames are in place but no planking is laid on yet. Others wait till the hull is planked up and then fit the stringers, fastening them through both frames and planking. Steaming them to bend them to the curve of the hull is not necessary. The stringers are usually bent along the turn of the bilge by force and held with clamps until the fastenings are driven.

In small craft up to 40 ft. or so there is no reason why the stringers should not be all in one piece, for pitch pine grows to a great height. In bigger yachts the stringers have to be in two or more lengths scarphed together. When the scarphs are long and well fitted and bolted, I believe there is only a slight loss of strength. These stringers help to tie up the hull longitudinally and to spread out from end to end the wringing strains when the yacht is sailing hard, or worse, dropping her bilge heavily on a hard sand.

Sailing vessels are subjected to far greater strains than many yachtsmen appear to realize. When a yacht is being sailed hard, for example, into a head sea consider the strains put on her hull by the sails alone : the wringing strain of the mast that tends to twist the boat at that point and which is aggravated by the tremendous upward pull on the weather topsides through the chain plates and backstays. There may be a severe upward pull of the various halyards on the deck beams around the mast if they belay on fife rails fastened to the deck ; and the upward drag of the bowsprit and forestay at the stem, the head sheet fairleads on the lee deck and the mainsheet horse are all trying to pull the hull out of shape.

Now add to these stresses, all of which of course are allowed for in the construction of the hull, the tremendous wringing strains caused by the sea itself. As the little ship lifts herself over a sea her bow for several feet may remain unsupported while the sea passes under her bilge. Then as she falls into the trough and plunges her bow into the next sea, the shock of the impact is transmitted back through stringers and deck and carlines to her stern, while the very buoyancy in her bow—the pressure of the water, that is, on her bow planking—strives to force up her head while the forward momentum of her mast and its rigging and sails is trying to drive her deeper. No wonder old yachts, especially old racing yachts, show signs of becoming 'hogged'—or their sheer line appreciably humped—in the way of the shrouds and runner plates, their seams cracked and showing and their entire hulls 'kinda tired looking'.

The bilge stringers are fastened, in small yachts, through the frames with copper rooves of a larger gauge than the ordinary frame fastenings. In big yachts they may be bolted to the frames. Some builders—Thornycrofts in their fine power cruisers, for example—make a practice of fitting two or even three stringers aside for the whole length of the vessel. These give excellent longitudinal strength and enable the frame scantlings to be lighter.

The beam shelves, another form of fore and aft stringer into which the ends of all the beams are fitted, are next fastened in place, and the work of fitting the beams can be begun. In very cheaply built craft, such as fishing boats, the ends of the beams merely rest on top of the shelves and are held by iron spikes driven into the shelves as in Fig. 3. The tendency of the beam to lose its camber (or 'round' or 'spring') and flatten out, in addition to the side (athwartship) thrust of the mast on the beams, is transmitted as a shearing strain to the single fastening at A. Needless to say, boats knocked together like that do not keep their shape long, and flattened deck beams, leaking decks and a general tendency to work is their legacy, even though the owner may proudly slap 4 in. by 4 in. deck beams and point to even more massive shelves and cry : 'Ah, they *built* these old fishing boats. Look at the size of these frames.'

A slight improvement is shown in Fig. 4 in which the beam end is cut and the side thrust is transmitted direct to the shelf, the fastening merely holding the beam end down on to the shelf.

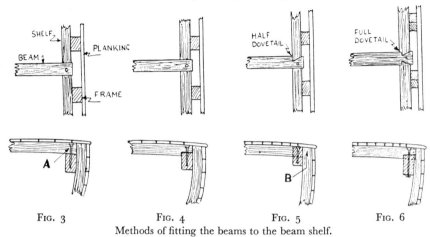

FIG. 3   FIG. 4   FIG. 5   FIG. 6
Methods of fitting the beams to the beam shelf.

The more usual yacht practice is the half-dovetail, shown in Fig. 5 which holds the beam from thrust to port and starboard, tying up a local strain transmitted to a few beams by the mast, for example, along the whole length of the beam shelf. But half-dovetailing of all beam

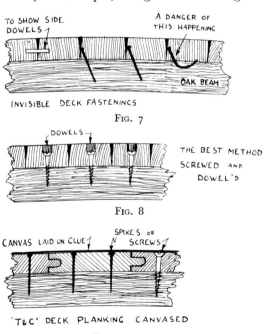

FIG. 7

FIG. 8

FIG. 9
Methods of fastening the deck planks.

ends (and of the inner ends of the 'half beams', or short beams, into the carlines) means labour, and if you insist on building a boat as cheaply as possible you must go to a builder who will pass such work as in Fig. 3. You get just what you pay for, no more, no less.

Fitting the top of the beam flush with the top of the beam shelf, as shown in Fig. 5, has one defect so far as the life of the yacht is concerned. It places the top of the shelf up against the underside of the deck—many builders make this a standard practice—and so traps air between the shelf and the planking at *B*. This air has no ventilation, and in time—ten, twenty years may be, but sooner or later—dry rot will set in, probably first in some of the frame heads. To obviate this and to ventilate behind the lining *above* the shelf, the beams should not be set quite flush with the shelf, as in Fig. 6.

With the beams and the carlines in, the deck can now be laid on. There are several ways of fastening a yacht's deck of which three examples are shown : Fig. 7 shows the 'invisible' method wherein the deck planks are fastened by spikes driven at an angle through their sides, the heads being covered by the seam caulking. Fig. 8 shows a more careful method by screwing, the screws being countersunk about $\frac{1}{2}$ in. and the holes plugged with carefully fitted dowels. These plugs should be cut so that the grain will appear parallel with the grain of the deck planks. Both these styles are for 'laid decks' of white or Kauri pine or silver spruce, bare and un-painted, and the seams have to be kept suitably caulked and payed with glue. Nice to look at, but devils to keep fresh and leak proof. Fig. 9 is the simple tongue and groove deal planking which is afterwards covered with canvas laid on to hot marine glue. No caulking of the seams is required and, except for occasional painting, this canvased deck requires almost no attention.

In yachts with 'laid' decks, the covering boards (the wide planks forming the outside edge of the deck along each side) and the king plank (the wide central plank from the stem and from the taffrail) are usually of teak, varnished, and the deck planks are either straight, or parallel to the king plank, or—if expense is no object—curved and parallel to the covering board. The 'sweep' of the latter method is very pleasing to the eye, and I expect many a yachtsman has taken a fancy to a yacht on the appearance of her nice, clean, curved decks.

If the yacht is to have bulwarks (instead of that bit of 2 in. teak 'footrail' that seems so inadequate when you are fighting to stow a staysail on a slippery, wildly plunging foredeck, so futile to catch hold of when your foot slips over it and you feel the cold rush of water closing over you, and yet looks so neat and tidy aboard any modern long-ended yacht while she lies at anchor) if, I say, your yacht is to have bulwarks, they must be properly fitted.

It is possible to fit a 6 in. rail with ash pegs driven down into the covering board and timber heads every 2 ft. or so, but it is not a strong job. Another way is to bring the ship's frames up through the covering board and to fasten the rail or bulwarks to them. This is a very strong job, but with one grave disadvantage : should a slight collision with another boat or a dock wall drive in the rail and break some of the frames, the hull is at once weakened and repairs will be heavier. It is better, therefore, not to extend the ship's frames through the covering board, but to fit separate 'rail timbers' alongside them, extending three or four planks down and holding the bulwarks above the deck (Fig. 10).

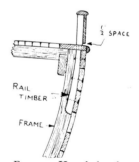

FIG. 10.—How bulwarks are fitted.

To give ventilation around these rail timbers where rain water would otherwise collect and begin rot, it is wise to leave a gap of about $\frac{1}{2}$ in. (some say $\frac{1}{8}$ in. and others $\frac{3}{4}$ in. ; take your choice) between the bottom of the rail and the deck. In the waist of the ship, where the water on deck will collect deepest, this gap may be increased to 1 in. for a rail up to 8 in. in height, so as to do away with extra scuppers. If the gap is made more than $\frac{1}{2}$ in. alongside the cockpit it becomes a nuisance, as it lets in too much cold draught on the weather side, and too many things are liable to slide through it to leeward. Bitter experience, my son, bitter experience !

The most usual method of fitting the coamings is shown in Fig. 11. The coaming is fastened to the inside of the carline with brass screws, countersunk and dowelled (though some 'cheap' builders don't trouble to dowel the screws, but merely stop with coloured putty). In Fig. 12 another method is shown. This economises in the width of plank needed for the coamings, as they are made to rest on top of the deck and are fastened through to the carline with ash pegs. In some boats—smacks for example—there are no carlines at all and the coamings are simply laid on to the innermost deck plank, as in Fig. 12 but pegged down to the ends of the half beams. This allows perhaps 2½ in. or 3 in. more headroom under the side decks between the beams, but it is a poor method of construction. A teak spline on the inside and a beading on the outside are needed in an attempt to stop leaks. They don't. This method of fitting coamings is weak and difficult to keep tight, and it is far better to pay for the use of a little more teak and have them fitted *inside* the carlines.

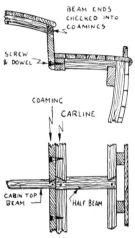

FIG. 11.—Two methods of fitting coamings.

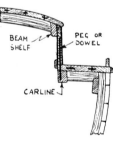

FIG. 12

The beams of the cabin top may be either ' checked ' into slots cut in the top of the coamings, as in Fig. 11, or half dovetailed, like the deck beams, into small size carlines inside the top of the coamings, as in Fig. 12. The coachroof may be laid like the deck, that is, with narrow planks, caulked and payed along the seams, or, more usually, with tongue-and-groove planks, canvased and painted.

Like the coachroof coamings, the forehatch has its own carlines and coamings, and a method I devised for avoiding that constant pest of all my previous boats—a forehatch that drips—is explained in another chapter.

The shroud plates may be fitted now that the rail and its capping are in place, and it is as well to see that the builder has ordered really ample size shroud plates, for a great deal depends on them. Much as I should prefer yellow metal plates so as to avoid the rust stains that eventually come from iron ones, I would still order galvanized iron plates ; for I have seen too many breakages with yellow metal plates. Only last summer I towed in a friend's boat which had been dismasted through the top of a yellow metal shroud plate fracturing in a squall. On examination I found the metal eye had had a slight fissure and gone green in the crack, but its presence was quite unsuspected until it broke—with the loss of the mast.

Unless you can get a guarantee that your plates are made according to the formula for Naval bronze I should advise ample size iron ones, and blow the comments of the club critics who say ' Shame to have iron chain plates on a nice yacht like that '. Poor yappers, their afternoon race in their one-designs and the evening in the cocktail bar don't give the same view as a blustering night off-shore in your own ship.

There is something to be said for the modern practice of bolting the chain plates on the *inside* of the frames. Neat topsides. Having said that I think you have covered its advantages. But provided the upward strain of the shrouds does not start a leak through your covering boards, nor shear the bolts away from the frame, it is effective in making your ship look neat and clean and modern.

The strain on weather shrouds and backstays in heavy weather is so great that special attention should be paid to the way it is distributed. I have come across—indeed, owned—

boats whose shroud plates were merely *screwed to the planking* by some builders who ought to have been—told about it. Screws shear sooner or later, and the planking also begins to pull through its own fastenings ; leaks start and, as in some cases, the whole shroud plate pulls out, lifting topstrake and deck !

The shroud and runner plates should always be through bolted each to one of the main frames, so that the upward pull is transmitted to the whole side of the ship down to the keel. If the hull is lightly framed with nothing but small steamed timbers throughout—too small to take a bolt—then the shroud plates should be long enough to be rooved with bronze (not copper) through fastenings to at least three planks and through bolted to the beam shelf. The same thing applies to bowsprit shroud plates (if any) and backstay plates : the strain should never be taken by the topside planking, but to frames or beam shelf, so that the load can be well distributed.

VIII

Engine Location and some Details

IT would seem that our ship is getting mighty near completion. She is planked and decked, her coachroof, hatches, rail, cockpit, chain plates, samson post—unless you have twins, when they become bitts—and so forth are all in place and the old man has probably by now caulked all the topside and bottom seams with white cotton and hardened in some 'patent stopping' over the top of it. Probably, in fact, the bottom has had one or more applications of creosote or other good wood preservative such as Cuprinol outside as well as in, and the topsides have their first coat of priming or flat paint. It looks as if the ship will 'soon be ready'. Experience of previous building jobs tells one that she won't.

If the engine is not already in place it darn well ought to be. The installation of the engine repays a great deal of extra care. The hard wood bearers on to which it is to be bolted should extend as far forward and aft as space allows. One or two engine manufacturers—British ones I am sorry to say—pride themselves on the shortness of their engines. They build them on the lines of the Empire State Building. The result is a tall, ungainly brute with a short, wide base that concentrates all the vibration and thumping blows on to two or three frames at most. The engine rocks, the whole ship vibrates, the bolts or coach screws on the bearers work loose, the shaft whips, and the stern bearings give trouble. Short, high engines are not ideal for work in yachts whatever fishermen may think of them.

In neatness and suitability of design for boat work American marine engines are nearly all points ahead of the majority of British marine engines. It is a hard fact that can make one a little sad. The American designers study the limitations imposed by boats with a fine run aft and pare off the tail end of their engines, shape their gear box, and restrict the depth of the oil sump, until the final design looks as though it really was planned to *fit* in the after end of a small hull. In building two sister ships to one of my designs I discovered that three well known makes of British marine engines of the power required (between 10 and 15 b.h.p.) could not even be fitted in at all where wanted while the neatest and best designed British engine of this power had to be placed 8 in. farther forward in one ship than the 20 h.p. American engine installed in the other. That 8 in. just spoilt the companionway.

When motor car manufacturers decide to storm the marine market for extra business ('This motor boating seems to be booming,' says the Great Man, 'we'll get our drawing office to make a marine job out of our standard unit') the result is little better than an honest, acknowledged car engine converted to marine use. One such engine I showed to an American friend at the Olympia Exhibition, a unit that looked as though the water pump, dynamo, carburettor, starting gear and other excrescences had been bolted to it as an afterthought, brought forth the undying comment : 'My Gaad, they sure stood well back when they slung the gadgets on that one !'

The inferiority in *outward* design or outline in so many British marine engines is not at all necessary, and is only pig-headedness and a lack of conception on the part of the designers. But because of it, hundreds of American marine engines leap the tariff wall every year and are installed in British boats, although in service the British engines may last for twenty years without wearing out, which is more than can be said of some others.

The less vibration a marine engine gives out, the better for the ship. The modern four-cylinder unit, designed expressly for marine work by a designer who has actually seen the inside of a sailing yacht, makes a very fine auxiliary, provided it is well installed. The bearers should rest on as many frames as possible and be bolted to at least two heavy floors. With a good quiet engine, properly installed, and with an efficient exhaust pipe line, it should be next to silent when running at half-throttle.

No petrol or paraffin engine is entirely free from oil drip, whatever the agents or the makers say, and I always insist on having a galvanized iron or copper tray underneath the whole engine, between the bearers, with a small drain sump from which accumulated oil can be pumped out. Many American engines have flame traps and trays beneath their carburettors as well as visible fuel filters fitted as standard. In England these necessary fittings in the majority of models have to be added by the owner, but they should not be omitted. A gauze-covered tray, forming a flame trap for spilled petrol, should always be fitted immediately beneath the carburettor.

The fuel pipe line should be easily visible from end to end, from the carburettor to the tank, and it should not be placed so that heavy articles, such as the kedge anchor, warps, navigation lamps, spare sails or boathook, can be stowed nearby and fall against it. The petrol tank should be well away from the engine, but placed so that its underside can be inspected, and the filler should be arranged either on deck or in the cockpit, where any overflow will drain away and *not* filter into the bilge.

The exhaust pipe should be carried up close to the deck at one point and thence led, without any right angle bends, to a convenient outlet. Personally I prefer the exhaust to be led out aft high enough to be clear of the water when the yacht settles her stern down at full speed—6 or 7 knots—but if a side outlet is preferred it is best to let the pipe join a T-piece leading to opposite sides of the ship. In this way, when the engine is running with the yacht heeling, the exhaust will have an open outlet whichever tack she is on. Unless the exhaust system is water-cooled, the pipe should be carefully lagged and kept as far away from the hull as possible. Leading the exhaust up a hollow mizen is not satisfactory : there is often much black oil and carbon blown out, and the result when it falls on deck—especially with a light following wind—is not conducive to white decks, ducks or DAKS.

Lubrication of the stern tube is generally neglected in auxiliary cruisers with excessive wear and hot bearings in an emergency as the result. Usually the stern tube is in an inaccessible place far up under the cockpit floor, and the greaser a small screw cap about the size of an old lady's thimble. I usually have the stern bearing drilled and tapped to take a pipe of $\frac{1}{4}$ in. or $\frac{5}{16}$ in. This pipe is led in as straight a line as possible forward to an accessible place on or near the engine, and a large size grease screw cap or even grease gun fitted. (Fig. 1). This pipe—and this is worth insisting upon—should be filled with the proper lubrication grease *before it is screwed into place.* Once there it is easy enough to force plenty of grease down into the stern tube with an occasional twist of the screw cap whenever one runs the engine.

Whether one decides to have a central or side propeller can form the subject for an inconclusive argument. Men have installed auxiliaries in old yachts with the propeller back of the

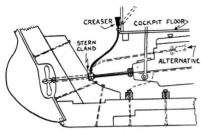

Fig. 1.—Two positions for an accessible stern bearing greaser.

stern post, cut huge gaps in their rudders, and complained bitterly that it has ruined their ship's sailing qualities. Others have felt wiser and fitted their propellers under the quarter so that no gap had to come out of the rudder, yet they, in due course, have complained bitterly that the drag of a big three-bladed screw has ruined their ship's sailing qualities. A doctor friend of mine had a central installation in his newly built modern type yawl, but the big gap the builder cut in his rudder caused the boat to be slow on the helm and uncertain in stays, and the owner said characteristically, 'I'll never have a central installation again.' It is a curious fact that most yachtsmen form their conclusions on one little occurrence or experience and proceed to damn every other idea.

What, then, is one to do ? It depends on the boat, the propeller and the gap.

Although the side installation works in a truer slip stream, for a sailing yacht I do not favour it for five reasons :

(1) The drag of a large propeller and *A* bracket. (It is as much as towing an ordinary bucket. You can try it at 6 knots, but make the lanyard fast.)

(2) The liability of the propeller to foul stray warps, and to damage.

(3) Its bad effect on steering when it is on the lee side, especially when handling the ship in canals and locks.

(4) The need to pierce the ship's planking and fit shaft logs over the hole.

(5) The torque given the helm when under power.

The only advantage of the quarter installation, as I understand it, is that the propeller works in a better flow and is therefore more efficient. But even if it loses, let us say, 20 per cent.

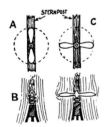

Fig. 2.—How 'dead' water follows the squared-off sternpost.

of efficiency by being centrally installed, I do not consider this a grave detriment in an auxiliary installation. If the central propeller gives the yacht 6 knots, it is doubtful whether the same engine and propeller installed on the port quarter would give her more than 6¼ knots.

A great deal of drag under sail is eliminated by using a two bladed propeller centrally installed, and marking the shaft inside so that it can be held with the propeller blades up and down behind the stern post (Fig. 2 *A*). A certain amount of vibration from the propeller is sometimes experienced where the stern post is wide and completely masks the blades. This is due to the column of 'dead' water which is dragged along by the after surface of the stern-post (*B*). At each half revolution the two blades pass from the free flowing stream (*C*), which has passed along the hull, into the stagnant water being dragged behind the square face of the stern post, and receive a slicing shock.

Not only does this cause vibration, but it also accounts for a considerable loss of efficiency, the exact amount depending largely on the width of the stern post and the size of the propeller blades. It is therefore very necessary to insist on having the after edge of the stern post well chamfered off in the way of the propeller blades, in other words to streamline its after face as much as possible. Because of the labour involved and the amount of wood to cut away, many builders dislike doing this.

Cutting too large a gap for the centrally installed propeller is a frequent cause of sluggishness on sailing yachts' helms. In some cases of old type long keeled yachts, which are slow on the helm in any case, such an aperture has caused them to miss stays with serious results in crowded rivers. The reason why builders generally cut out a bigger hole than the propeller itself needs to work in is the outside gland of the stern tube. Fig. 3 shows a typical installation and gap, both in rudder and stern post, as many builders will make it unless you stand over them with a sledge hammer. Engine manufacturers themselves do not make it easy by attempting any economy of length in most outside gland fittings (D). I have seen scores of yachts with apertures as large as the one illustrated, and when the yacht is sailing and the helm is put over, it will be seen how much of the stream that should impinge on the rudder blade will escape through the gap. If the square, unchamfered face of a stern post, which may be 4½ in. in width, adds its own turbulence to what little stream is left to reach the upper part of the rudder, the poor crippled yacht is almost bound to miss stays under difficult conditions of wind and sea.

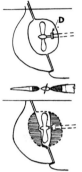

FIG. 3.—How a propeller gap can be filled up and 'streamlined.'

But both the propeller vibration and the helm sluggishness can be almost entirely eliminated by the simple process of filling up all unnecessary space, leaving just enough for the propeller to work in, and by streamlining not only the after face of the stern deadwood but also the leading face of the rudder stock on to which the propeller stream impinges. Fig. 3 shows how filling pieces may reduce the propeller aperture to the minimum and at the same time allow a much less disturbed flow to the propeller and to the rudder. These filling pieces may be either of wood, spiked or fastened with small brass straps, or they can even be of sheet brass cut and bent to shape and screwed to stern post and rudder blade.

If this shaping process is properly carried out there should be little loss in propeller efficiency over a quarter installation, and no appreciable effect on the yacht's sailing qualities.

The engine may be installed now but it will not be finally coupled up to its shaft until the vessel is afloat and has 'settled herself'. Then it will be time to line up the engine by inserting thin copper discs (shims) between the bed plate and its bearers where necessary so as to get the crank shaft exactly in line with the propeller shaft. Ships, even small yachts, alter their shape slightly when they leave the slipway and become water borne, and an engine installation that was perfectly aligned while the yacht was still blocked up in the builder's shed would probably be straining once the yacht was afloat, and a hot stern bearing would be the normal result.

With the bulkheads, cabin settees, lockers, doors, galley, plate racks, shelves, floorboards and the plumbing completed and in position below decks the little ship is nearly ready for launching, and she is now taken out of the shed, to make room, may be, for the next yacht whose keel will be laid in a day or so. If, as in some model yards, the slipway or main railway runs right up out of the water into the shed—as, for example, at Herreshoff's or in Silvers' in Scotland —the almost completed hull will have been rolled or slid along and work on the next boat to occupy her berth in the building shed will have begun a week or more back. In small yards where they have no particular slipway, a temporary slip is laid down to slide the boat into the water. Heavy wooden troughs, well greased with tallow, are laid, one under each bilge, and the chocks holding the ship up are transferred, one after the other, so as to rest the weight on the greased ways. With tackles, a good deal of hard breathing and maybe a cuss word or two (New England or Old England, the words are similar and mighty effective) the yacht is slid by jerks along the ways to the end. Then the ways over which she has been pulled are taken up and laid again in front of her and the process of track lifting and laying goes on until the boat reaches low water mark. After that it remains only for the tide to rise and, lo ! she is water borne.

Depending on the facilities at the yard, the masts are stepped either on the slipway outside the shed, by a derrick or a pair of sheerlegs placed for the purpose, or after the hull has been launched. At the more primitive yards where only small craft are built the latter is the more usual procedure, and a local smacksman may be asked to lend his boat for the purpose—in exchange for a ' lick o' paint ' or maybe a pint or two. The smack's gaff is used as a derrick and the mast, with a sling just above its centre of gravity (very well, just over half way up) is lowered cautiously into the hole which the builder should have remembered to have cut in the deck for the purpose. What would happen if at this juncture it was found that Old Tom had ' clean forgot about that there mast hole ', is worth contemplating.

The disadvantage of waiting until the yacht is afloat before stepping the mast is that a breeze of wind will render it impossible, maybe for several days. A mast can do a surprising amount of damage to the deck and deck beams when it is being stepped in a hull that is jumping about. It is therefore very advisable to choose a calm day for the purpose.

And now the ship is afloat, her spars are aboard and in place, and Old Fred is ' a riggin' of her up ' with his plough steel wire and manila purchases ; and the sails, after all that tele-graphing, have arrived and are ready to be bent, and there's a general scent of lovely new cut wood in the cabin—not that sour, mouldy, keroseney, aged odour of an old ill-kept boat—and the burgee will be at the masthead as soon as Old Fred's boy Jim has climbed up there and rove the halyards, and before long the sails will be set and drawing and we shall be able to see if she does sail like a witch. . . .

Even if she is not quite the perfect dream-ship you have visualized for years, it will not matter. The joy and satisfaction of planning a lovely thing like a cruising yacht, and of watch-ing her grow until she is there beneath you, with her guiding helm in your own hand, trembling with the life that you, her creator, have given her—why it is the most satisfying thing in the world. And only one thing is better : to go and create another ship even better and more beautiful in a few years' time.

And now let us turn to some shoal draught designs that others have created, and study their curves and forms and—faults.

76

PART TWO
Some Shoal Draught Cruisers

' Over the seas and far away.'

I—VIVETTE II

12-Tons T.M.

LOA	- -	35 ft. 9 in.
LWL	- -	28 ft.
Beam	- -	10 ft. 4 in.
Draught	- -	3 ft. 6 in. (ex C.B.)
		6 ft. 6 in. (with C.B.)
Iron keel	- -	3.25 tons
Ballast (inside)	-	Nil
Sail area	- -	619 sq. ft.
Designer	-	Fredk. Shepherd, M.I.N.A.
Builder	-	Harry King & Son, Pin Mill, Suffolk, 1936
Owner	-	Mr. F. E. S. Lindley
Auxiliary power:		2 cyl. 7½-9 h.p. Kelvin on starboard quarter.

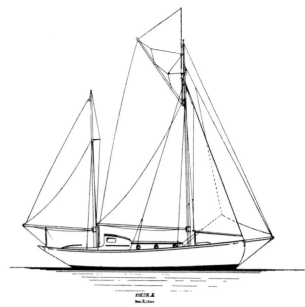

Vivette's singlehanded ketch rig totals 619 sq. ft.

CRUISING yachts designed by Fredk. Shepherd are very familiar to English yachtsmen. According to *Lloyd's Register* it appears that Fred. Shepherd has been responsible for no fewer than seventy yachts, all of them cruisers, ranging from 4 to 142 tons. I have never yet come across an ugly boat from Shepherd's board (although every designer, however successful, occasionally produces a somewhat *plain* boat for owner's reasons), while the majority of his designs are very fine, shapely and able craft indeed, boats that one naturally wants to call 'chesty' or 'husky' according to which side of the Atlantic you are. Shepherd's boats are characterized by very buoyant bow sections, ample freeboard, a pleasing sheer line, an absence of any rubbing strake, somewhat full quarters, good, roomy accommodation with a straightforward and well tried layout, and a comparatively heavy displacement.

Of all these designs I believe only two have been of light draught centreboarders : *Corona*, 31 tons, designed and built in 1911, and *Vivette II* a new creation of last year. Although this latter centreboarder is different in many ways from his usual designs, *Vivette* shows many of the well known characteristics of Shepherd's work : the full bow with the neat curve of stem for example, the short, elliptical counter stern, the full quarters, the generous freeboard and the flush topsides without any 'rubber' or mouldings. The raised deck companion is a fairly modern feature of Shepherd's boats and in this case gives not only a great deal of added space, light and air below (over the galley where it is most needed) but it has enabled the owner to arrange a most convenient seat where one can sit in comfort and in the dry and see what is happening all around. The only disadvantage to a deck companion of this kind that reaches the *full* width of the coach-roof is that its height and width obstruct the view of the helmsman unless he sits well out on the weather coaming, or stands at the helm. This is why personally I prefer the hatch companion that is no taller nor wider than it need be.

The centreboard and construction of its case, together with the accommodation layout below decks, is largely the owner's idea, and to me it

Vivette looks sturdy afloat.

looks essentially practical. For a boat where a paid hand will not be carried the toilet, in my opinion, is in the right place. The navigator's berth opposite the galley is a canvas 'root' bunk. The canvas bottom is attached to a round spar which fits into chocks on each bulkhead; two or three chocks

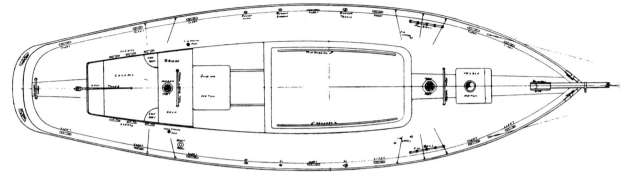

Vivette's deck plan allows plenty of room—and plenty to hold on to.

are placed in various positions so that one can have either a fairly tight canvas bottom or, for heavy weather, one that sags and so forms a comfortable trough in which to sleep. *Dorade* has canvas berths of this type.

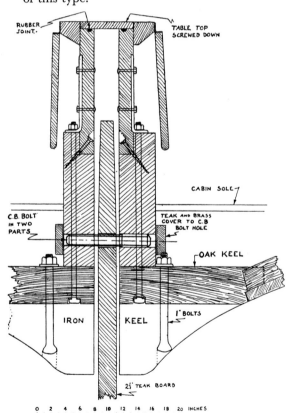

Construction details of *Vivette's* C.B. case to plans by the owner.

The spaciousness below decks can be judged from the plans. Good freeboard, over 10 ft. beam and full sections, with a floor width of some 3 ft. 6 in. between the berths result in one of the roomiest 12-tonners I have seen. The lack of hanging space in the plans has been settled since the lines were laid down by the addition of a large hanging clothes locker on the port side of the saloon at the fore end, and the removal of the wash basin to enable the berth to come aft to the bulkhead. In place of the two fo'c'sle cots a single built-in berth has been substituted, so that the ship sleeps four in comfort. The masts are in tabernacles, the mainmast coming down to one side of the mizen and the main crosstrees swivelling to allow for this. The mizen mast folds forward.

The most interesting features of this boat are the width of the English elm keel, which is 3 ft. 10½ in. amidships, and the centreboard and its construction. The board itself is built up of three planks of teak, varying from 2¾ in. to 2¼ in. in thickness. Sandwiched between them are strips of ⅜ in. iron of the same width as the teak. These iron strips are calculated to resist some of the bending strain to which the board is subjected when lowered and also to help to sink the board, which would otherwise be inclined to float.

Many designers and owners appear to have no conception of the tremendous side thrust that is transmitted to a centreboard or plate when lowered with the ship sailing hard in a seaway. That is why so many steel or iron plates get wrung and begin to jam in the keel slot or the case. To

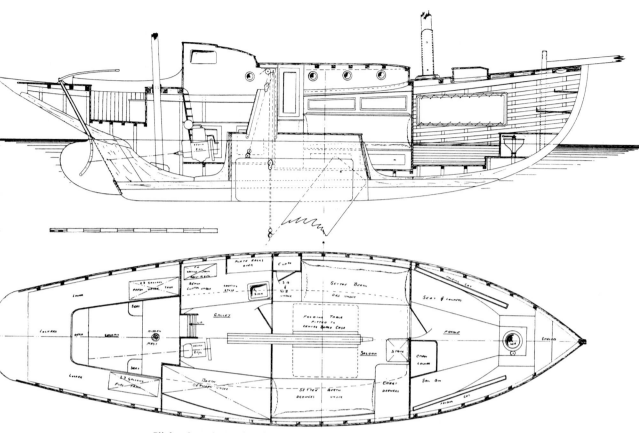

Slight alterations—described in the text—were made to this lay-out.

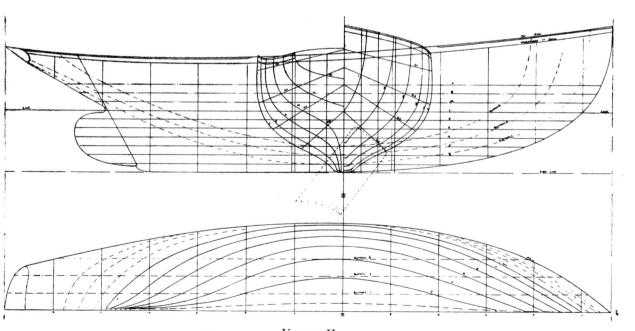

VIVETTE II
Full bow sections and full quarters give her a stiff and roomy hull.

be of sufficient strength not to bend under even the worst conditions, an iron plate should be so thick that its weight makes it a continual strain on the bolt and tackle and the very devil to raise. That is why American builders with their wider experience of C.B. craft scarcely ever think of using a metal plate, except for racing purposes.

Vivette II's owner—who previously owned Keeble Chatterton's old 4-tonner *Vivette*—has given much thought to the C.B. and case, and his knowledge as an engineer was more than useful. The teak board with its iron reinforcing has a calculated negative buoyancy of about 60 lb., of which only some 40 lb. should rest on the lanyard, so that this board ought to be raised by hand *without any tackle*. If it were a $\frac{5}{8}$ in. mild steel plate instead its weight would be more in the region of $3\frac{1}{2}$ cwt. or 400 lb. and at least a 6 to 1 purchase or a mighty powerful winch would be required to raise it, with all the attendant troubles of a very heavy centreplate.

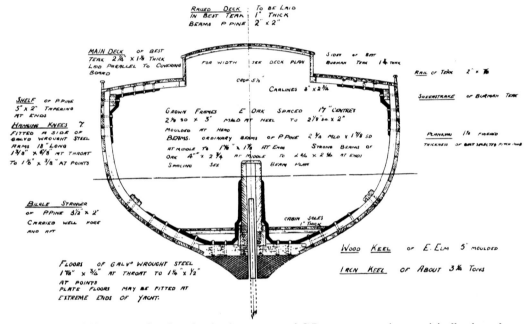

Vivette's midship construction data showing iron straps and C.B. case construction as originally planned.

As the board is so strong and rigid and leaves an ample area of itself within the keel slot and case even if the lanyard is let go and it drops right down, Mr. Lindley has not worried about a stop bolt to prevent this. He considers that by running the ship into shoal water the board will not fail to be pushed up, when the after part of the case (arranged for the purpose) can be removed and the lanyard retrieved. As the top of the case has been kept well above the LWL it may be removed while the yacht is afloat, and the large clearances between the ends of the board and the keel slot may quite easily be poked clear of accumulated mud with an iron bar. The strong construction of the C.B. case—of 4 in. teak—is shown in the diagram on page 80.

Vivette II handles well without her C.B. and even turns to windward satisfactorily in a decent breeze without it, but the sloping sides of the keel and fullness of the garboards naturally allow her to sidle away to leeward in a light breeze. The C.B. however stops this and *Vivette* gives her owner every satisfaction on a peg to windward. One may remark that this C.B. installation has been well thought out, and if it gives the owner any trouble I for one shall feel surprised.

2—HAR JEFF

A 10-Ton Keel Sloop

LOA -	- 29 ft.	Displacement	7·5 tons	Designer	- E. P. Hart, Poole, Dorset
LWL -	- 24 ft.	Lead Keel	- 2·25 tons	Builder	- Harry Feltham, Portsmouth, 1936
Beam -	- 10 ft.	Ballast -	- Nil	Owner	- M. R. Berney
Draught	- 3 ft. 3 in.	Sail area	- 429 sq. ft.		

IN this design for a keel boat of very limited draught, Mr. E. P. Hart has done a clever piece of work. Ostensibly planned to suit the conditions of Portsmouth Harbour and its creeks, and Chichester, Christchurch and Poole harbours, *Har Jeff* should also be able to face any coastal passage in reasonable weather and not be afraid of crossing to Cherbourg or Boulogne when required.

To eyes accustomed to 6 ft. draught and a lot of forefoot, her profile may appear to have far too little lateral plane for windward work. But, has it ? Let us look at the line of her stem as it travels from the LWL downwards. There is a good deal of ' leading edge ' there down to the forward underside of the iron keel. Remember, it is not by any means merely the *area* of lateral plane that keeps a yacht from sagging away to leeward. When a boat with a deep forefoot and a straight level keel is sailing, the water becomes agitated at the passage of the forefoot and at once gets dragged along with the hull and the keel in a state of turbulence. Much of the water on the lee-side of the keel—the side that matters when planning to reduce leeway—is pressed down and underneath the garboards, to rise in a hump of turbulence under the vessel's lee quarter. Now with a deep forefoot the whole length of keel and the garboards above are passing through water which has already become disturbed and set into a forward motion by the friction of the part of the hull which has already passed through it.

It is more effective therefore to take a longer ' slice ' at undisturbed water, and just as the leading edge—about 20 per cent. of the total width—of both an aeroplane's wings and of a yacht's sails when sailing close-hauled—is the most effective in lift and drive respectively, so the leading edge of a hull is the most effective part for reducing leeway.

In a hull whose draught is strictly limited it is obviously a problem to know how to gain an effective length of leading edge to assist the lateral resistance. In most cases, of course, a centreboard is the solution and usually a satisfactory one. Here, too, the leading edge of the centreboard when fully lowered should not be vertical but at an angle, so that, within its limit of maximum draught it has the greatest possible length of leading edge.

In *Har Jeff* Mr. Hart has not only given his design as long a forefoot as could reasonably be gained, but he continues some of its effectiveness by sloping his keel aft, so that the bottom of the keel is meeting fresh and comparatively undisturbed water right down to the heel. These lines reveal some careful thought and a knowledge of how to get the best out of a hull of limited depth. Mr. E. P. Hart is an old hand at shoal draught hulls, being, I think, the sole professional British yacht designer who has devoted some thirty years to the study of this subject, and he has been .working along the line of developing a hull with very light draught which will at the same time be reasonably efficient at windward work without a centreboard. There are several Hart-designed boats in and around Portsmouth harbour.

Har Jeff's forward sections show great buoyancy, added to which there is a great deal of ' pick up ' in the forward overhang, the buoyancy of which comes into play as soon as the bow hits a sea.

If the mast appears tall—as it is for a boat of only 3 ft. 3 in. draught—the initial stability in those full shoulders and hard bilges, in the ample beam alone, will take care of that, and I cannot imagine that buoyant head being driven down by the weight aloft of a tall mast.

The sudden little turn to the garboards should be noticed in the middle sections. Most designers in planning this hull would have had no reverse curve in the garboards at all : they would have brought them in to the keel at the angle of the outer strakes with a hard rabbet line, or angle, all along the keel. *Har Jeff's* sections mean stronger construction and a little more labour in shaping the garboards and the frame ends ; but they also mean a very slightly faster boat, since there is a little less

83

HAR JEFF

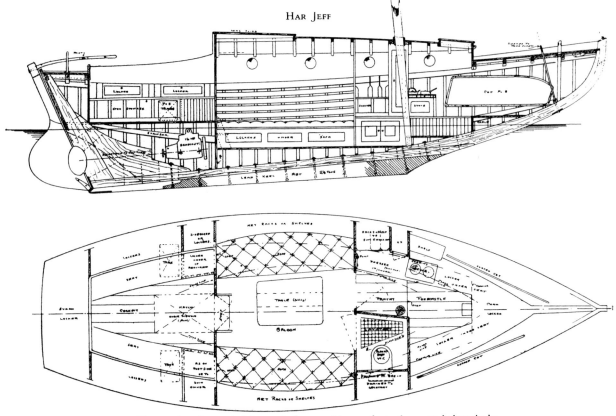

The coachroof extended forward of mast adds greatly to the room below decks.

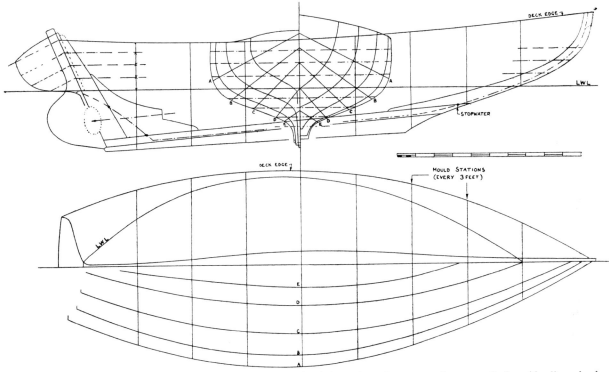

With 10 ft. beam and a fixed draught aft of only 3 ft. 3 in., the designer has taken every advantage of a long 'leading edge.'

wetted surface in the garboards; and one other feature which is important in shallow boats—a place where the bilge water will be collected and easily pumped out. It is always a problem in a boat with fairly flat sections and no reverse curve to the garboards to know how to overcome the nuisance of bilge water that has nowhere to go and prefers the lee settee.

Below decks *Har Jeff* is straightforward and conventional for an English design. The cockpit is large and roomy with a central companion leading into a short saloon with the usual settee berths. The galley is to port alongside the mast. Opposite is an enclosed lavatory. Without any desire to criticize the layout I think there is a shortage of interior locker and clothes hanging space which would be acutely felt in wet weather if all four berths were occupied. Unless the boat were to be used only as a day cruiser it would seem preferable to extend the coachroof aft to the petrol tank and to have a full length clothes locker on one side and, say, a sideboard the other.

The rig is simple and easy to handle with its single headsail of only 91 sq. ft. A fine and effective Genoa could be set on hanks on the head stay. Provided that in gybing hastily the mainboom end does not try conclusions with a conceivably slack backstay, the mainsail would be docile and easy to set, reef with the roller gear and furl.

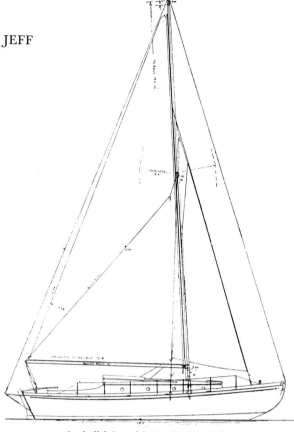

An ' all inboard ' rig suits *Har Jeff*.

I understand that *Har Jeff* has shown a clean pair of heels with the wind at all free. This is to be expected when we look at the clean lines of her hull and the small amount of wetted surface to drag through the water. Boats of this shoal type with buoyant bows to help to 'keep their heads up' can attain remarkable speeds given the right conditions and on occasion can easily run away from a deep and heavy displacement boat of the same WL length.

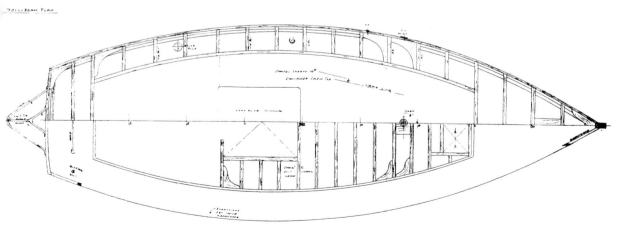

Har Jeff's deck plan. A solid outrigger for the main backstay is incorporated.

3—TASIA, A DALLIMORE 10-TONNER

LOA - - 33 ft.
LWL - - 27 ft.
Beam - - 9 ft.
Draught - 4 ft. 6 in. (ex C.P.)
          6 ft. 6 in. (with C.P.)
Lead keel - 3 tons
Displacement 8·5 tons (approx.)
Designer - Norman E. Dallimore, Burnham-on-
            Crouch
Builders - H. King & Son, Pin Mill, Suffolk, 1937
Owner   - J. W. Campbell

SOME twenty-five yachts have been built to designs by Dallimore, who must be England's leading amateur designer. *Tasia* is the third that he has designed and had built for Mr. J. W. Campbell and she shows all the good features of a Dallimore keel yacht.

Unlike an American design for a centre-boarder of this size she has a fairly deep body with a generous displacement, and at the same time her beam is that of a deep keel yacht. She is narrower, deeper and probably a little heavier than a boat of her general size would be in the United States,

A neat rig for solo-sailing.

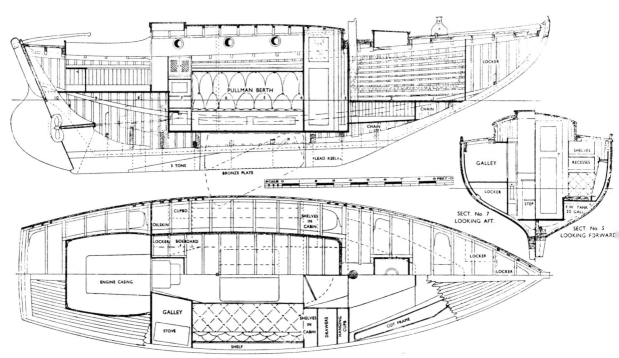

Tasia's layout plan is orthodox for an English sloop.

By courtesy of *The Motor Boat*

86

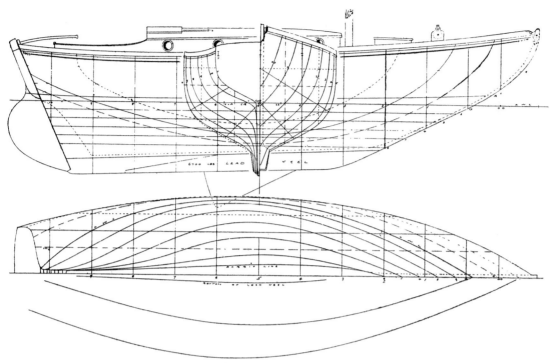

The lines reveal the comparatively deep and full body.

and with her quite ample draught of 4 ft. 6 in. the centreplate should prove unnecessary for most circumstances. It would be only when trying to beat against a short, steep sea or in light baffling head winds that the plate would prove its worth.

The centreplate is housed entirely beneath the cabin sole and is of $\frac{1}{2}$ in. bronze. There is a radial slot and stop bolt to prevent accidents (wise designer !) and the pivot bolt passes through the lead keel. The pendant chain passes up through a neat brass tube to a simple tackle on the cabin top.

The engine, a Gray 4-22, is installed out of sight beneath the cockpit floor and gives a speed of about $6\frac{1}{2}$ knots. Stationed in Poole harbour in Dorset, this little cruiser is a good example of a keel yacht with a centreplate for occasional use.

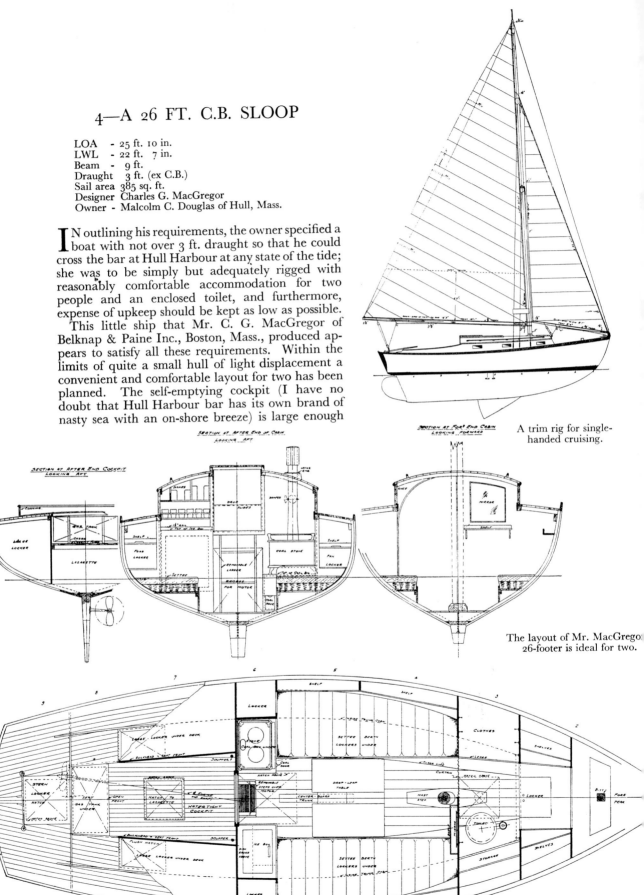

4—A 26 FT. C.B. SLOOP

LOA - 25 ft. 10 in.
LWL - 22 ft. 7 in.
Beam - 9 ft.
Draught 3 ft. (ex C.B.)
Sail area 385 sq. ft.
Designer Charles G. MacGregor
Owner - Malcolm C. Douglas of Hull, Mass.

IN outlining his requirements, the owner specified a boat with not over 3 ft. draught so that he could cross the bar at Hull Harbour at any state of the tide; she was to be simply but adequately rigged with reasonably comfortable accommodation for two people and an enclosed toilet, and furthermore, expense of upkeep should be kept as low as possible.

This little ship that Mr. C. G. MacGregor of Belknap & Paine Inc., Boston, Mass., produced appears to satisfy all these requirements. Within the limits of quite a small hull of light displacement a convenient and comfortable layout for two has been planned. The self-emptying cockpit (I have no doubt that Hull Harbour bar has its own brand of nasty sea with an on-shore breeze) is large enough

A trim rig for single-handed cruising.

The layout of Mr. MacGregor 26-footer is ideal for two.

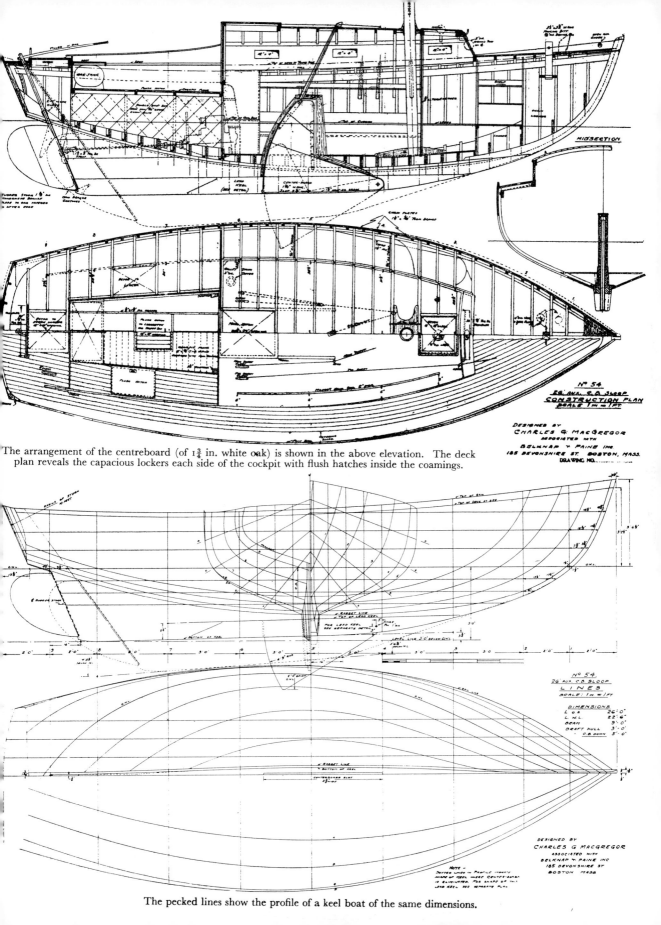

The arrangement of the centreboard (of 1¾ in. white oak) is shown in the above elevation. The deck plan reveals the capacious lockers each side of the cockpit with flush hatches inside the coamings.

The pecked lines show the profile of a keel boat of the same dimensions.

for a day party of four or five, as it measures 6 ft. 3 in. by some 5 ft. with 2 ft. 5 in. width of floor space at the after end. It is just long enough to sleep in should hot weather make it desirable, yet being a self-drainer it is not a source of danger to the yacht in a breaking sea. Because the cockpit floor stretches to each side of the ship some roomy lockers are available under the side decks.

The galley, with its coal range over the coal box, and the ice chest opposite with various lockers for foodstuffs are in a convenient place in this size of cruiser. The shelves for crockery and glasses are shown on the after bulkhead over the ice box. Forward there is a good size hanging clothes locker behind a curtain with a toilet to starboard and another big locker and shelves forward again. The well-cambered coachroof, which gives headroom under its beams, comes forward of the mast and gives headroom also in this lobby.

A week's cruising in wet weather aboard this little ship for two people would prove how much space and stowage room she has, and how little real inconvenience would be occasioned by bad weather in consequence.

The centreboard trunk forms a support for the drop-leaf table, and except for its extension aft of the table, is not at all in the way. Even without the C.B. this little hooker ought to turn to windward satisfactorily with that efficient rig, for her midship section is very similar to that of my old *Nightfall*, and she was no sluggard at windward work in any breeze. The garboards meet the keel all along in a ' hard rabbet line ' and there is an ample amount of vertical lateral surface in the deadwoods aft— as the section through the after end of the cockpit shows.

A duplicate is being built for Mr. Norman E. Lee of Jersey City, but *Liza Lee IV*, as she is to be named, has the keel dropped 9 in. and no centreboard. I understand such a boat can be built at a small local yard for around $2,000 exclusive of engine, but inclusive of lead keel, bronze screw fastenings and mahogany deck fittings and interior trimmings.

Boats of this general type ought to be much more popular in England than they are, and the price might possibly be a little less.

5—RETRIEVER

CROCKER-DESIGNED C.B. YAWL

LOA   - 30 ft.
LWL   - 24·2 ft.
Beam - 10·4 ft.
Draught   3 ft. (ex C.B.)
            5 ft. (C.B. down)
Sail area 596 sq. ft.
Designer S. S. Crocker, Jr.
Builder - S. F. McFarland, South Bristol, Maine

Retriever

FOR this competent and shapely little cruising yawl with her easy bow and broad, powerful stern, I cannot do more than quote what Mr. Arthur Rotch, for whom *Retriever* was built, wrote me about her.

'*Retriever* is, I think, a remarkable little vessel' (writes Mr. Rotch). 'Mr. Crocker designed her for me in the fall of 1928. He was given a free hand except for the draught and approximate dimensions. She was built that fall and winter by S. F. McFarland of South Bristol, Maine, who is a descendant of a long line of builders of the famous Friendship sloops. I have subsequently sailed the boat for eight seasons and under all kinds of conditions. She has never failed to do what was asked of her, nor has ever caused me the least uneasiness. I have only had, at times, a mild curiosity as to how hard it was going to blow.

'First and foremost she is an exceptionally able sea boat. My previous boat was a Friendship sloop of almost identical size. These boats, as you may know, have an enviable reputation for extreme ability. There is no possible doubt that the yawl was the superior in rough water. I attribute it to her light displacement and shoal draught which enabled her to give way to a breaking sea.

Retriever's galley is light and airy

'Secondly, she is an extremely handy boat. With the wind from two points abaft the beam to ahead she will steer herself, though she required careful sail trimming to do so. You could tack her by casting off the jib sheet and hauling it in again when she was about. She never failed to stay, no matter how rough the water. When running before it, in any reasonable sea, you can put the helm down, let her come around through the wind and be off on the other gybe without touching a sheet. This manoeuvreability enables you to take her into the most crowded places without worry.

'I usually sailed her alone and often cruised singlehanded or with my wife in her. She will heave-to very nicely under mizen alone with the helm half up or with the mizen hard in, jib out a little and helm nearly amidships. On one occasion in a high sea I hove-to to go below and check my

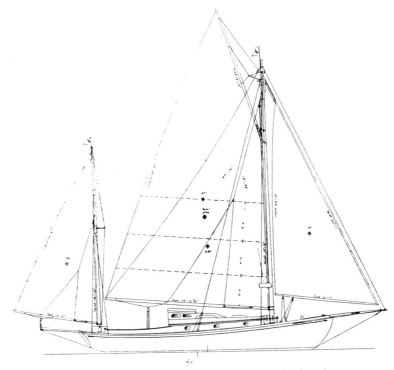

Retriever carries an ample cruising rig of 596 sq. ft.

tides and get lunch. After getting under way again I went out on the bowsprit and spent some time there clearing the jib down-haul which had gotten adrift. She lay like a duck, forging ahead slightly and making a square drift.

'She is quite a fast boat and shows up particularly well to windward in a hard breeze and rough water. My brother-in-law has an Alden ketch designed as an improved *Svaap*, 34 ft. on deck, 29 ft. waterline, and we have sailed a good deal in company. His boat is Bermudian rigged with 650 sq. ft. of sail. In light airs he has the best of it, but in strong winds and rough water to windward the *Retriever* leaves him very easily and is much more comfortable.

'I have entered her in the Jeffries Ledge Race a number of times and she has done very well, winning in her class in 1932. This race starts from Manchester, Mass., goes to a buoy off the back of Cape Cod, then 55 miles north to a buoy on Jeffries Ledge some 35-40 miles off shore and return, a total distance of about 140 miles, all in the open sea.

'On one occasion, when running before a strong north-westerly breeze from Jeffries Ledge to Peaked Hill Bay, the other mark of the course, we held a 55-ft. Alden schooner, a frequent Bermuda contestant, and at least once a prize winner to 35 minutes over the 55 miles and actually gained an hour over a 43 ft. Alden schooner. The seas were just wrong for the larger boats and the breeze was too strong for any light stuff. I checked afterwards and found we got light sails on as soon as anyone.

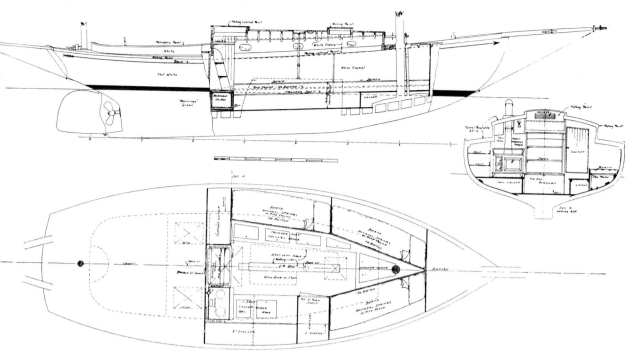

The large self-emptying cockpit is typical in American cruising yachts.

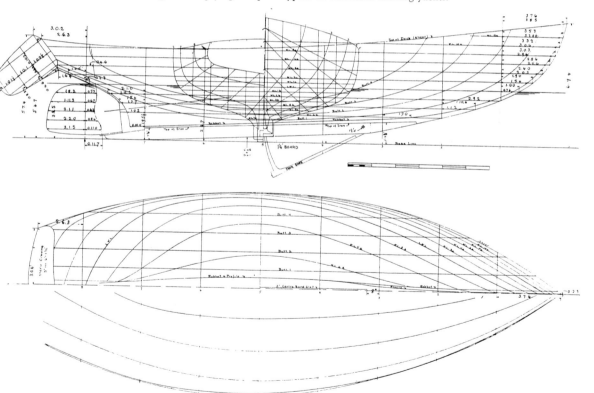

Retriever's lines reveal a sweet hull with generous beam and plenty of sail-carrying power.

Incidentally, I kept the wheel for the whole run, which shows how nicely she handled, as some of the schooners were wearing out a helmsman in half an hour. I know *Retriever* is the smallest boat ever to win this race, and I think the smallest ever to finish it.

' On another occasion, the bearing for our compass had got knocked adrift and we were unable to find the Ledge buoy. We were coming home against a strong south-wester with all sail. When daylight came, we saw the *Niña* which you know (Hammond's boat) and a large ketch fighting it out for first place in the large class and both well reefed down. We decided that if they who were racing found it necessary to reef, we who were not had better do likewise.

' I mention all these things to show that the little boat is no fair weather craft but well able to take care of herself off shore, although she was not designed for that sort of work.

' Her maximum speed is very high and on a run or a broad reach, she frequently does her $7\frac{1}{2}$ knots, and on one or two glorious occasions has bettered that considerably. On the wind with a fresh breeze she will do 5 knots within $4\frac{1}{2}$ points and $5\frac{1}{2}$-6 knots within 5 points. Closer than $4\frac{1}{2}$ points is barely practicable. If there is a decent breeze she *never* has to be helped out with the motor to get to windward, no matter how rough it is. This is not true of most small cruising boats on this side of the " pond." I know a lot of Crocker boats and they all seem to have this ability, which I attribute to their long buttock lines which hold them down to their work.

' Her motor is a Gray 4-30 turning an 18×10 two-bladed feathering wheel. She has a comfortable cruising speed of 6 knots at about 800 r.p.m. and a fuel consumption of about $\frac{3}{4}$ gallon per hour. Her maximum is $7\frac{1}{4}$-$\frac{1}{2}$, though at this speed the engine gives quite a hum that I never could stand for long. She has power enough for almost any emergency, which to my mind is important. If you are going to put up with power in a boat, I am all in favour of having plenty.

' The interior accommodations speak for themselves. A toilet was installed between the two forward bunks and a curtain across the after end of them. A chart locker was built at the forward end of the seat by the stove. The large engine-room was my insistence, and very useful as a " catch all " in a hurry. She is as tight as the day she was launched and never makes water no matter how rough the going. This again is due, I think, to her light displacement and ease in a seaway.

' The centreboard has given no trouble and no leaks. If I were building again, however, I think I would take the board out and give her 6 in. more draught which would be ample as I never needed the whole board. I think I would also incorporate the little deckhouse companion, shown in the latest sail plan sent you. Very much like your own, by the way.

' I know yachtsmen on your side are suspicious of wide boats and *Retriever* must look very odd to your eyes. I do not think though that you have had experience with a properly designed beamy boat. There are very few of them and it seems to require a special knack. However they are such comfortable craft and sail at such small angles of heel and I cannot see that a *well designed* one loses any sailing efficiency. My favourite sailing ground is south of Cape Cod, an area of fresh winds, strong tides and shoal water with a natural result of short steep seas which you would think would be the enemy of a wide boat. Yet the type developed there was the Cape Cod Cat, a boat of two beams to her length, and very clever sailers these boats are if well designed. I owned one once and enjoyed her immensely.

' This has turned into a terrificly long letter, but I am incorrigible when on the subject of boats and then too, being a married man with a family, I have no time to use a boat so I have just sold *Retriever* to Mr. W. Brewster Bunnell of Hingham, Mass., and have consequently enjoyed talking of her. In praise of Mr. Crocker who is an artist at his work, and far too modest a man to make a great name for himself, I may mention that Mr. Bunnell had had one Crocker boat and wanted another and I got myself another Crocker boat, a little 22-footer drawing 2 ft. 6 in., something like your Lymington " L " class designed by Laurent Giles. I have noticed that once a man has had a Crocker designed boat, he rarely has use for any other ! '

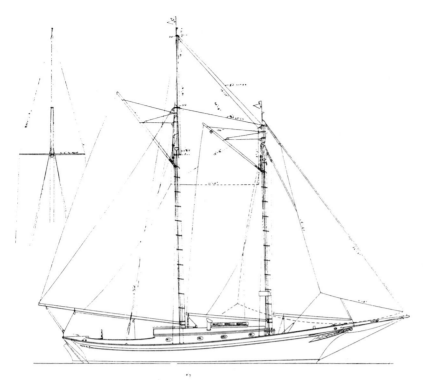

Aunt Sara carries 700 sq. ft. in her four lowers.

6—AUNT SARA OF COHASSET

A 35-FT. KEEL SCHOONER

LOA - 35 ft.	Draught 4 ft.	Designer S. S. Crocker, Jr.
LWL - 28 ft. 7 in.	Sail area 700 sq. ft.	Builder - F. D. Rolfe, Quincy, Mass.
Beam - 10 ft. 10 in.	Power - Gray 4-40.	Owner - Lucius T. Hill, Boston, Mass.

IT is said there is no accounting for taste, and if I were to confess that this little 35-ft. schooner attracts me in one way at least more than any other design in this book I should expect many readers to feel incredulous. I do not say I should go so far as to build her, for we have to do far too much beating to windward around the English coasts for a rig like this ; all I say is that I think *Aunt Sara* has a curious charm of her own, and I enjoyed it to the full when, as a guest during a sweltering August week-end, I sailed with her owner out of her home port, delightful Cohasset Harbour, into the crowded anchorage of Marblehead.

Perhaps a little of the attraction—apart from the charm of any very small schooner whose rig looks well balanced—lies in the shapely clipper bow. It has always been a source of regret to me that this graceful type of stem has gone out of fashion. I know its weakness, the difficulty of getting sufficient buoyancy and bearing without making the bow look full and ugly : but I still hold to the opinion that given the gaff schooner rig, the right type of hull, the right sheer line and the right colouring, a well-proportioned schooner bow, with a correctly proportioned design of fiddlehead and scroll work, is one of the most satisfying bows to look at from a dinghy. And it is also a fine, dry bow to punch into a seaway. It needs, I know, a short counter stern to balance it and to finish off the gold sheer line with another little piece of scroll work ; and *Aunt Sara's* broad transom, well rounded as it is, does not quite make the balance perfect.

But putting these objections aside, who amongst my readers would *not* get a certain satisfaction from just looking at a little schooner like this *Aunt Sara*, and from sailing her into an anchorage of slim modern long-snouted yachts ? Complicated rig, miles of halyards, deadly slow to windward, expensive in gear : I know all the objections. Yet I cannot help looking at these plans and photographs after a week-end aboard her, and declaring ' Yes, yes, but what fun it all was ! '

AUNT SARA

Aunt Sara's designer is something of a genius in the design of shoal draught cruising boats, and like so many Americans, he has an unerring eye for line and proportion. This little schooner and the more modern looking yawl *Retriever* are boats of widely differing types, but both are from his board, and both are splendidly satisfactory in their different ways. A sister ship was built to the lines of the schooner for Dr. E. P. Hussey, the 'grand old man' of the Buffalo Yacht Club, who in his 88th year built her as a permanent home on the Great Lakes. *Falcon*, however, is ketch rigged with a white hull, and to my eye does not look nearly so enchanting as the same boat schooner rigged with a black hull. Which, of course, is all prejudice, dating back to the days when pirates were pirates and pirate ships were black schooners, and you know very well that you, my honest reader, would love to own a black schooner and go privateering as much as I should. Come now !

Who wouldn't like to blow into an anchorage at her wheel ?

The schooner was built for Mr. Lucius T. Hill of Boston in the fall of 1929, and in order to reduce the expenses of hull upkeep to the minimum there is no varnish work at all on deck with the exception of the spars. To reduce glare in the lovely sunshine of Massachusetts Bay the decks and cabin top are dark green and the hatches are painted a subdued reddish brown. Below, of course, cream white predominates.

Some idea of the spaciousness of the interior can be gleaned from the plans ; 10 ft. 10 in. beam has its advantages. There are four berths and the galley with its coal range, its sink, ice chest and crockery lockers is so arranged that the cook wedges himself against the mainmast with the left foot against the fore and aft bulkhead and the right against the sink locker and cooks while the ship busts her way through a snorter. And this ship, with her great beam and sturdy bilges, does not sail at an uncomfortable angle. She stands on her feet and does not throw everything out of the weather lockers or the pots and pans out of the galley as many of the deep-keeled, narrow-gutted, cramped little cruisers do.

The whole of the forepeak is given over to hanging and storage space and ship's gear, so that four people may cruise in comfort without that distressing untidiness in the cabin that is the result of a lack of space for clothes and suitcases.

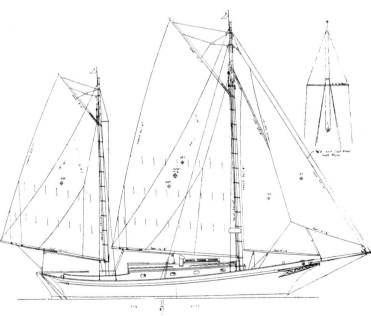

As a bald-headed ketch *Falcon* is not nearly so picturesque.

96

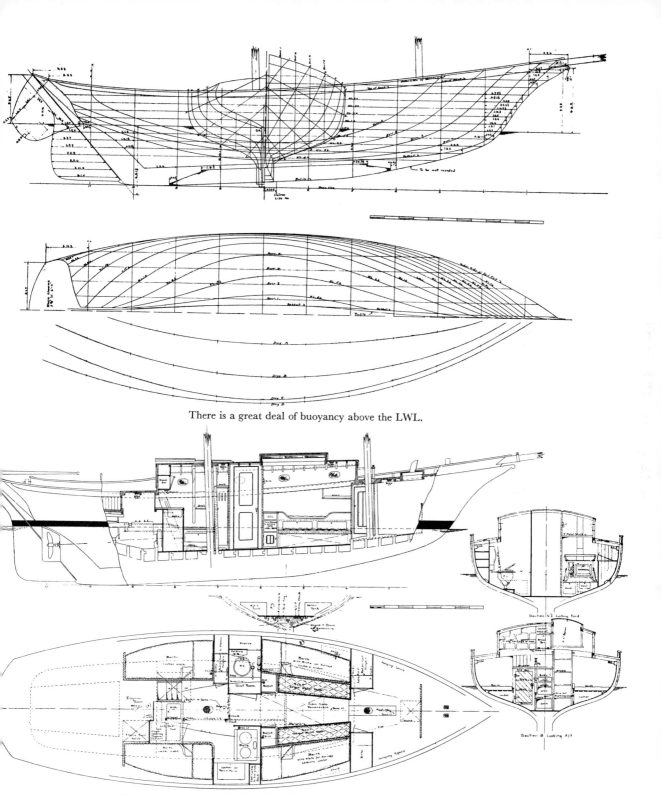

There is a great deal of buoyancy above the LWL.

The generous beam and full body combine to give a roomy lay-out below decks.

97

There is also a hanging locker in the after cabin where wet oilskins may be hung up to drain. Two 30 gallon fresh water tanks are arranged beneath the transom seats in the saloon and the various electric light points (domes) are located in the plans.

With her keel and after deadwood *Aunt Sara* has enough lateral plane to make her reasonably good to windward in a breeze, but this type of boat always shows up badly in light breezes when on a wind. True, the Gray 4-40 will drive her at a steady 7 knots—her maximum economical speed, although she would, on occasion, do nearly 8—but, like most of us, Mr. Hill says 'I'm always glad when I can shut off the noise of an engine.' Undoubtedly this schooner's windward qualities would be improved by the addition of a centreboard, but the layout forward of the mainmast would probably have to be rearranged to accommodate the trunk.

That *Aunt Sara* is a grand little sea boat and well able to take care of herself in a blow is borne out by her owner, who tells me :

'The worst weather we have been out in was a fifty-mile gale two summers ago in Buzzards Bay, which builds up a very steep sea. We carried the fore staysail and double-reefed main with three of us aboard, one of them a lady. We were entirely comfortable at all times and quite dry. No water came into the cockpit, although we ran dead before it for a time and expected that one of the short seas might break over the taffrail at any time. We were able to eat up to windward with this rig, although I wouldn't have wanted to claw off a lee shore under these same conditions in the middle of the night.

Plenty of space on *Sara's* deck.

'I am sure of my wind velocity on this day, as I checked with the weather bureau the following morning. Also, getting into port I started up the engine, and it was necessary to run at almost full speed to hold our own.

'With a fresh to strong wind off-shore on the beam and all four lowers set she has logged 8 knots for two hours on end. This must be the maximum speed of this hull.

'In light airs *Aunt Sara* does surprisingly well. Her worst point of sailing, naturally, is to windward, and she will not approach the performance of the modern cutter rigs. However, Mr. Crocker and I were working toward the so-called "motor-sailer" and were willing to sacrifice this point of sailing for the shoal draught and other features. Also, I am not a complete blue water sailor and confess to becoming thoroughly fed up after four or five hours banging into it.'

All I can add is that, during a particularly scorching week-end with a light head wind, I found that *Sara* would sail herself indefinitely with no one at the wheel—which is just the thing I like a boat to be able to do when I am supposed to be on watch. I cannot abide the boat that is like a frantic horse and behaves the fool unless you constantly watch her. *Aunt Sara* knew her job and just seemed to look after her crew.

7—WATERLILY II

28-Ft. C.B. Motor-Sailer. 6-Tons T.M.

LOA	-	- 28 ft. 3 in.
LWL	-	- 23 ft. 3 in.
Beam	-	- 8 ft. 3 in.
Draught	-	- 3 ft. (ex C.B.)
		6 ft. (with C.B.)
Lead keel		- 1·2 tons
Ballast (inside)		Nil
Sail area	-	- 350 sq. ft.
Designer	-	- E. H. French
Builder	-	- E. F. Elkins, Christchurch,
		Hants, 1937
Owner	-	- Major F. Stevens

In building, the sail area was slightly increased.

ONE of the worst problems in building small sailing cruisers under about 25 ft. LWL is to secure full sitting headroom over the saloon settees. Wide side decks—24 in. or so—between coachroof coamings and rail are the desire of most owners, but unless you make a little ship ugly with excessive freeboard the carlines will probably be too low for anyone but a dwarf to sit under them. Pushing the cabin sides farther out may enable you to sit up under the coachroof and perhaps locate the folded berth or some useful lockers under what deck is left. But on deck the danger of working a ship with only a narrow catwalk each side of the cabin top is ever present ; and nobody likes narrow plank ways.

Now this competent design for a 28-ft. C.B. yawl ' motor-sailer ' shows how a man who has, I believe, designed more power cruisers than sailing boats tackled the problem of wide side decks and a crick in the neck *versus* sitting headroom and a catwalk on deck. Mr. French has just extended the sides of his coachroof until they have become flush with his topsides, rather in the style of Mr. Henry Howard's famous *Alice*. At the same time the high raised foredeck of the motor cruiser with the excessive windage is avoided by bringing the coamings together just forward of the mainmast.

In setting and stowing the mainsail and reefing, one has to prance about on the cabin top, and there is no weather deck along which one can creep when going forward under way in heavy weather ; but the main hatch and skylight should give foothold and the handrail a fair hand hold, while the canvas-covered deck need never become slippery. Some owners say that painted canvas decks invariably become dangerously slippery after a time, but there are special ' rough surface ' paints on the market now (usually paint mixed with very fine silver sand) that make decks entirely slip proof.

Because one has to walk over the cabin top every time one goes forward its camber is limited to not more than about $\frac{3}{4}$ in. round to the foot of beam, so that the ultimate headroom over the cabin sole (or floor) will not be so much as could be obtained with cambered side decks and the same height of coamings with a much more sharply rounded roof. But unless one can stand up the only thing that matters below decks is that there should be full, unobstructed sitting headroom on the saloon settees. This little yawl has that, while the headroom under the beams over the sole is 4 ft. 7½ in.

The hull is full-lined and buoyant and, viewed from forward, has a particularly full bow. For reasons of economy in building the overhangs are kept short. The price complete with engine was limited to £500 with a reasonably expensive specification. I think it is to the credit of the builder that this little vessel can, I understand, be duplicated for about the same figure. Since the rig needs no bowsprit or boomkin aft what use would any longer overhangs be in a small cruiser like this ?

The centreplate, of galvanized mild steel, is a modification of the Albert Strange 'L' type (Fig. 3 in Chapter II). The tackle, which is shown leading to the mast tabernacle, is always inspectable and, in the case of breakage, could be renewed even at sea while the plate remained in its normal lowered position. A fillet piece with rubber insertion fits over the slot in the top of the case when the plate is up or down to exclude any splashes from inside the case, and the latter is utilized for the table flaps.

WATERLILY II

Because the raised deck extends forward of the mainmast there is ample sitting headroom in the fo'c'sle, which is curtained off from the saloon. The full bow sections give an air of spaciousness and, in a more practical way, enable a good full-size built-in berth to be on the starboard side. All the construction is of high-class work with 1 in. pitch pine planking copper roove to alternate grown oak frames and bent American elm timbers, and the cockpit coamings, seats, hatches, rails and cabin sides are of varnished teak. The 8-10 h.p. twin cylinder two stroke Stuart Turner engine is installed beneath a hatch in the cockpit floor, while the 8-ft. pram dinghy stows on chocks on the raised deck.

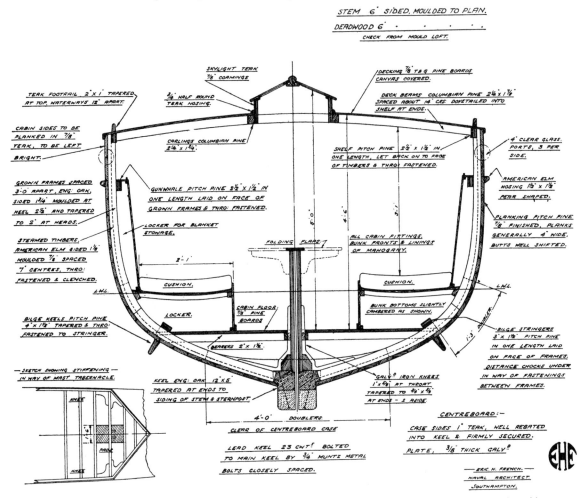

Waterlily's midship section showing scantlings, centreplate case construction and the extra room given by taking the cabin top out to the sides.

Waterlily II is stationed at Christchurch, Hampshire, where she is eminently suited to the local conditions. She is conspicuous in the anchorage on account of her bright yellow topsides and, as one might suspect, is known locally as 'The Yellow Peril.' I asked Mr. French how he developed her design and he writes :

' In the first place Major F. Stevens (the owner) had been looking round for some sort of shallow draught cruiser with an engine and centreboard that would meet with the conditions prevailing in Christchurch Harbour.

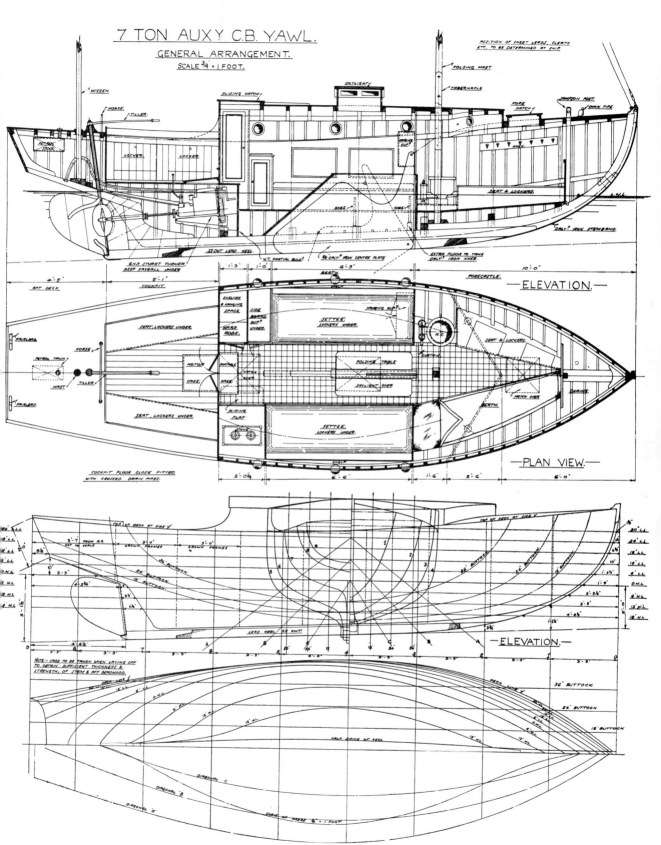

Waterlily's hull is full in the ends and generally well rounded.

' At the same time he wanted a boat that would sail with a fair turn of speed and give him a certain amount of comfort below.

' The boat was to be built at a figure under £500 but to be strongly constructed of good materials on grown frames. He had found a boat which he thought would be something like the type he required and the owner's permission was obtained to inspect the craft and take some rough measurements, which we did.

' However, whilst we were doing this we discovered many things that would not suit on the new ship-to-be, and the inspection ended with a long list of do's and don't's.

' I prepared an outline plan on the lines which we had discussed, with a small galley and two settee berths and a w.c. forward, rigged as a yawl with a folding mast and a cabin top amidships, but a fixed mast is fitted in place of the folding one now.

' At this time some drawings appeared in *The Yachting Monthly* of a very attractive shallow draught cruiser which had various points which appealed to us very much, and this design influenced the new plans to some extent.

' We adopted the same type of built-up topsides, as we found this would give clear sitting headroom over the berths, and make the saloon more roomy ; however, it did away with side decks and would mean going over the cabin top to get forward. All these points were weighed up and it was decided on for the reason of comfort below, and in any case the boat was not going to be built for speed, so comfort won the day.

' As a matter of fact this arrangement looks very well and makes a great deal of extra room below deck, as the cabin sides are in varnished teak. When she is afloat, it is impossible from a short distance off to see whether there are side decks or not.

' Half way through, the design was altered as she had so far been designed with a transom stern ; we decided, however, that if it were carried out into a short sawn-off counter we should get a better run-off aft and save drag. This was adopted and added a lot to the looks of the boat. It was also due to much discussion and consideration of a large number of the smaller points, that the accommodation was laid out and berths for three persons obtained with reasonable comfort. It was decided not to box the w.c. in, so that there would be more room and plenty of air space.

' The boat is fairly full in the bow and has a good run aft, slightly cod's-head and mackerel-tail appearance, which should help her in a breeze and help to make her dry.

' She is strongly constructed and will be able to take the ground at any time without damage, and owing to her fairly full bilge she will not lie over at an excessive angle and will lift easily on a rising tide.

' The finished boat though rather unusual is most attractive and promises a fair turn of speed ; she will at least provide her owner with a comfortable home afloat and should give him many pleasant cruises.

' She was not so much a design, as a result of ideas carefully thought out and then altered and sometimes altered again, so that the results should be good in an all-round manner; perhaps she will not be very special on any particular point, but taken bye and large should give comfort and satisfaction.

' It will be most interesting to know what her performance will be, but in any case she proved a most absorbing task to plan out.'

8—THE THREE BROTHERS
OF MIAMI

LOA   - 44 ft.
LWL   - 38 ft. 11 in.
Beam - 13 ft.
Draught 5 ft.
Sail area 1102 sq. ft.
Power - 32-40 b.h.p. Buda Diesel with 2:1 reduction
           gear
Speed - 8 knots
Designer Frederic A. Fenger
Builders- Oscar Blumquist, Blue Island, Ill., 1935
Owner - Ralph G. Hutchins

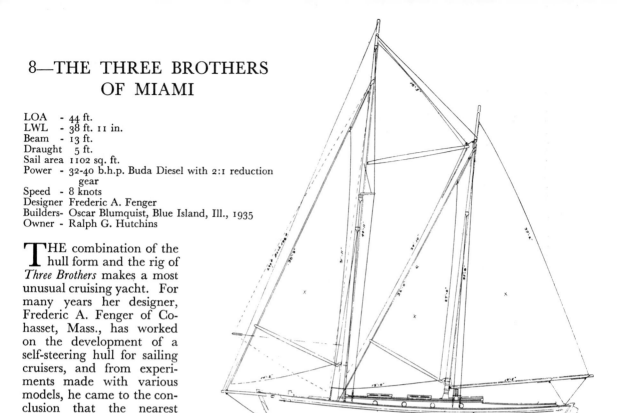

The 'main trysail' rig—shown here on *Three Brothers*—was introduced by
Mr. Frederic A. Fenger.

THE combination of the hull form and the rig of *Three Brothers* makes a most unusual cruising yacht. For many years her designer, Frederic A. Fenger of Cohasset, Mass., has worked on the development of a self-steering hull for sailing cruisers, and from experiments made with various models, he came to the conclusion that the nearest approach to the ideal had been attained by those wonderful lateeners of the Red Sea, the Arab dhows. Fenger, then, is the advocate of the 'dhow-type' hull in the United States, and the hull-form of *Three Brothers* will be seen to have the main characteristics and general lines of a dhow.

In the matter of the 'main trysail' rig, Fenger was the first to introduce what has since been loosely known as the Vamarie or Wishbone rig in its entirety. For many years he experimented with divided booms and spars in models and evolved through these models the rig shown here.

That both the hull form and the rig are entirely successful is borne out by the enthusiastic owner who, after bringing *Three Brothers* down the Mississippi from Lake Michigan to the Gulf of Florida, plans to cruise in her along the coasts of South America. As the ship was built of timber of which every piece had been seasoned for at least three years, and as her scantlings are very rugged—planking 1⅝ in. Douglas fir, steamed oak frames 2½ in. by 3 in. every 12 in. and keel 14 in. moulded in one piece with a lengthy iron keel stiffening it—this main trysail ketch ought to stand up to any conditions likely to be met.

I cannot do better than give the designer's own reasons for his choice of hull and rig, which he has been kind enough to write specially for this book :

THE NEW 'DHOW'-TYPE HULL AND THE 'MAIN-TRYSAIL' RIG

A sporting old buffer from Chowes
Was commanding his craft from the bhows.
Asked, ' Is it a yacht ?
He replied, ' No, it's nacht.
I've always been partial to dhows.'
—Punch, August 5, 1936

On the other hand, Huxley once said, ' Science is nothing but trained and organized common sense, differing from the latter only as a veteran may differ from a raw recruit.' In this new hull development, then, the underlying thought was to solve, as far as possible, and from a common sense viewpoint yet quite without reference to any previously existing type, what may be called the ' conflict of centres ', *i.e.* the rather disproportionate ranges of the centres of lateral resistance and buoyancy in relation to the centre of effort of the sail plan, under varying conditions of speed and course, in order not only to obtain better hull balance but also relatively more speed and weatherliness. So far as we know them, the investigation was to be based upon sound principles of design and practice.

Although the writer was then a devotee of the schooner rig in its old form, the gaff-headed ketch rig was tentatively selected as having perhaps a more equal fore-and-aft distribution of effective unit areas for the purpose in mind. It may be of interest to note that in the final rig development, a new form of schooner-ketch was evolved. Directly under the centre of effort of each sail, a proportionate

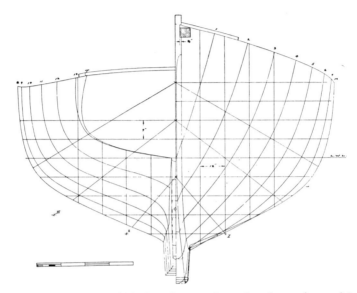

The body plan of *Three Brothers* which shows her easy forward sections and powerful quarters.

area of lateral resistance was placed, and when these were joined together they formed a contour having a rather deep forefoot from which the keel raked *upwards*, in reverse drag, towards the stern. This contour—somewhat resembling that of the Arabian dhow, though more correctly the patamar—immediately suggested a method of streamlining by which the centres of buoyancy and lateral resistance might be located considerably forward of their more orthodox positions, thus shortening their potential ranges of travel which usually are greater than that of the centre of effort of the sail plan.

So far as it has been carried out, the actual streamlining has been in the nature of an attempt to marry a load waterline, both upright and heeled, that will cause a minimum of surface disturbance, to an underbody in which the successive lower waterplanes increasingly are filled out forward while their after ends become correspondingly more concave.

Such a hull, with its relatively finer run having a somewhat diminishing lateral plane under it, not only is left to ' find ' itself on its natural turning centre which is well forward of amidships, but also required only two-thirds of the usual rudder area and far less potential helm angle both in manoeuvring and holding a prescribed course. Thus the lead of the centre of effort of the sail plan over the centre of lateral resistance has been reduced to a minimum which may actually approach zero when these centres more closely are approximated through new formulae. It may be added that new formulae or methods of approximation *were* devised (based upon rising wind pressures aloft and increasing lateral resistance as the keel extends into deeper and less disturbed water) and that these formulae checked with the known performance of vessels of ordinary design. When properly balanced as to sail plan, the tendency of the new hull form decidedly is toward self-sailing, the rudder remaining idle from close-hauled to started sheets, and having a small amount of fixed helm when the wind is

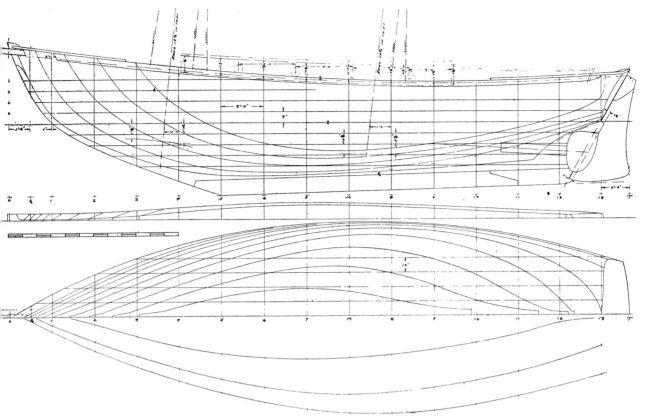

The lines of *Three Brothers* are Mr. Fenger's rendering of the Arabian dhow hull for a yacht of limited draught.

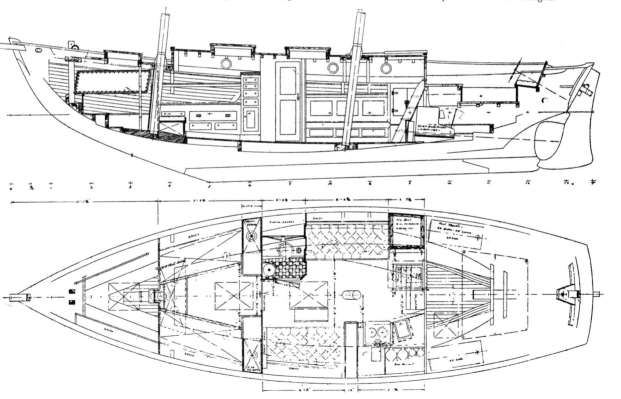

The layout of this 44-footer shows the amount of space available in the above hull.

brought from abeam to the quarter. The sheets are trimmed as in ordinary sailing, the headsails not being flattened for ' steering ' purposes.

Going to windward, the vessel is held on by the deep ' V ' sections of her forebody and the forward cutting edge of the stem as it slopes rather steeply downward from the entrance to the ' toe ' of the keel. In the fully developed form, these forebody sections strongly resemble the mid-sections of the old English cutters. From the ' toe ' aft, the remainder of the keel functions partly as additional lateral area—the reverse drag following as closely as possible the drift of the ' keel water ' as the Danes call it—and also as a damper against minor tendencies to affect the vessel's course. There is an eating to weather and in squally breezes, when sudden heeling grows to knock-down proportions, the vessel eases herself in a series of pilot's luffs but without losing her wind.

In contemplating this contour, it must be remembered that unless directly before the wind, the water strikes the keel at an angle to leeward of the course. The indications are that in this hull form, the lateral plane may be somewhat reduced in area while, draught for draught, the centre of gravity of the shoe or outside ballast lies somewhat lower than in an ordinary vessel—excepting that with a straight keel which is parallel to the waterline—as the shoe width is greatest through its deeper length.

With a normal entrance and a somewhat increased residual buoyancy throughout the forebody, the tendency is to reduce ' stamping', the hull motion being in a more nearly vertical direction rather than short pitching around its point of gyration.

Off wind, an obvious comment is that the deep ' toe ', fairly well forward, will cause the hull to gripe and, more particularly, to take charge when running directly before it in a heavy sea. This is not the case, however, in a properly designed hull. For with her flattened buttocks and relatively fine run, the stern tends to *follow* the fore end, in a manner of speaking, rather than to push it. This was first proven in model trials and subsequently borne out in actual practice.

In this connexion, it has been the writer's experience that if kept fairly upright, a well balanced hull should not be particularly affected by the onslaught of large following seas, *per se*, even when they strike at an angle. Yawing, or rounding-to, seems to be brought about more directly through the violent change in the immersed form as heeling suddenly increases and the arm of the centre of effort is as suddenly lengthened. Whether one may agree in this matter or not, there is considerable support for the use of the reverse drag as worked out in this type, under severe conditions in a following wind and sea. When brought into play, the rudder no longer is forced to shove the deepest area of the lateral plane hard over in order to prevent the vessel from coming-to, and there is a gain in effective leverage. In short, there are all the advantages of the long keel but with a short turning radius.

Due to her owner's requirements for comparatively shoal draught without a centreboard, the example shown is but a modified form of the new hull type. But despite her generous beam, which is somewhat tempered by easy bilges and flaring topsides, she shows comparatively deep slicing forward sections, and while her keel is but 16½ in. deep at the ' toe ' and even less through her middle sections, she has been an excellent performer to windward. This is due almost entirely to her foregripe, and although she is very moderately streamlined, her centres of buoyancy and lateral plane are somewhat forward of their orthodox positions. As in the more fully developed form, she steers ' by the head', with a minimum of helm and rudder area. Thus she holds to the traits of the out-and-out ' Dhow '-type, and although her owner neglected properly to rake her masts, his claim is that she ' sails herself hour after hour.'

In the nature of a by-product from the designer's hull-form investigations the main-trysail rig primarily was an attempt more fully to utilise the area between the main and mizen masts of the old gaff-headed ketch and thus to obtain an adequate spread in the more modern form, without extending the masts to unreasonable heights for offshore work. During the early model trials, made nearly ten years ago, it was found that this inverted trysail on the mainmast—now known as the main-trysail—was surprisingly efficient at all angles of heel, having more apparent tractive effort and less depressant effect than any other sail.

Upon this premise, the rig seemed well worth serious development. A fairly narrow mast spacing was indicated, somewhat less than one-third the overall length of the vessel, allowing considerable latitude in proportioning the end sails. As for balance, it was obvious that, taking into account the windage of masts and rigging, the mizen should be of generous area in order to furnish adequate drive, in what we call a ' hard chance', when the rig is reduced to the two end sails.

The rig should neither be in yawl nor true ketch form, but more nearly that of a schooner-ketch.

In turn, the individual sail units conformed with their corresponding units of lateral resistance in the underbody contour, due allowance being made for advance in the effective centres concerned. The proportions were worked out so that as canvas successively was reduced through a No. 2 main-trysail, to the three 'lowers' and finally the end sails, the centre of effort moving slightly aft as it came downward, balance was maintained with the retreating centres of the underbody.

Hand in hand with this sizable mizen—larger than those which have been variously applied by other designers—the tendency toward 'drift ahead' on the part of the masts was materially reduced, and there has been far less need for a permanent backstay which, after all, must usually be supplemented by runners. In the designer's later developments—not here shown—the mizen stay has been homed slightly abaft the main mast, to a thwartship traveller known as the 'bear trap' on which the tack of the mizen staysail may be shot to leeward for lifting effect when on the wind in a half gale; or slewed to weather as the sheets are eased, in order to catch more breeze and create a better draught under the lee of the mizen.

The original purpose of the 'bear trap' was to allow the use of a small club at the tack of the main-trysail so that its longish foot more easily might be flattened in order to regulate the draught in the lower portion of the sail. And when the mizen staysail is stood to windward, there is more space for handing the main-trysail under its lee.

More important, however, is the fact that through the use of this 'inset' mizen stay, a very considerable aftward drift can be made in the main intermediate shrouds so that this mast may now stand quite independently of the mizen and its runners or backstays. Under this latter method of staying, the main mast need not be quite as stout as that of equal length for the ordinary marconi rig. This affords the advantage somewhat of increasing the diameter of the mizen mast so that the spar weights are brought farther aft to reduce pitching, while the mizen runners need not be used till the wind has grown nearly to gale force.

And so it has been a step by step development in which many new problems and stresses were encountered and had to be solved. Common sense dictated that the main-trysail sprit—an adaptation of the well known 'split-sprit' used over forty years ago in the old New Haven sharpies—*must* come down with its sail and be stowed on deck when not in use. As an old windjammer put it, 'You reef your yards and tops'ls from deck!' Actually, the rig is reefless, and one need not run into the wind to shorten down.

Years before the conception of this new hull and rig, there lay the age-old intrigue some day to create an offshore vessel of more than pocket size in which one might carry on regardless, snug down at a hand's turn, spread light canvas to suit one's yen for flying kites, and gain such respite from wheel and watch that one might more fully enjoy the moods of the sea while finding one's way upon it with sextant and chronometer.

For the original articles, see 'The Dhow Type'—*Yachting*, February 1927, and 'The Main-Trysail Rig'—*Yachting*, August 1926.

9—NORMA

5-Ton C.B. Sloop

LOA	- - -	24 ft.
LWL	- - -	21 ft. 6 in.
Beam	- -	8 ft. 6 in.
Draught	- -	2 ft. 5 in. (ex C.P.)
		5 ft. 6 in. (with C.P.)
Displacement	-	4 tons
Ballast (inside)	-	1·7 tons
Thames Tonnage	5	
Designer	- -	Reg. F. Freeman
Builders	- -	T. H. Turner, Leigh-on-Sea, Essex

*N*ORMA was built for use on the South-end shore, where yachts take hard ground unprotected in the prevailing onshore S.W. winds.

Mr. Reg. Freeman, a local naval architect, has designed several boats of this type, and *Norma* is a fairly typical example of a successful small English cruiser with the ' open pen-knife' or ' L' type centreplate. *Norma* is now stationed in Margate harbour, where she again dries out on a hard bottom.

The interior is quite simple and straightforward, and *Norma* can be used either as a day boat or as a small week-end cruiser for two. The cost to duplicate such a boat locally would be in the region of £300 ex-motor.

Norma's snug sail plan totals 310 sq. ft.

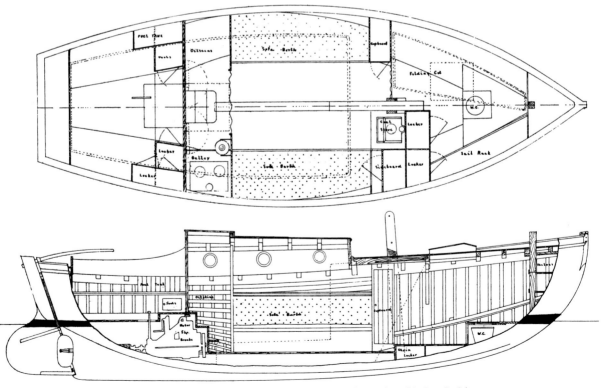

The layout is compact and simple. The headroom in cabin is 4 ft. 6 in.

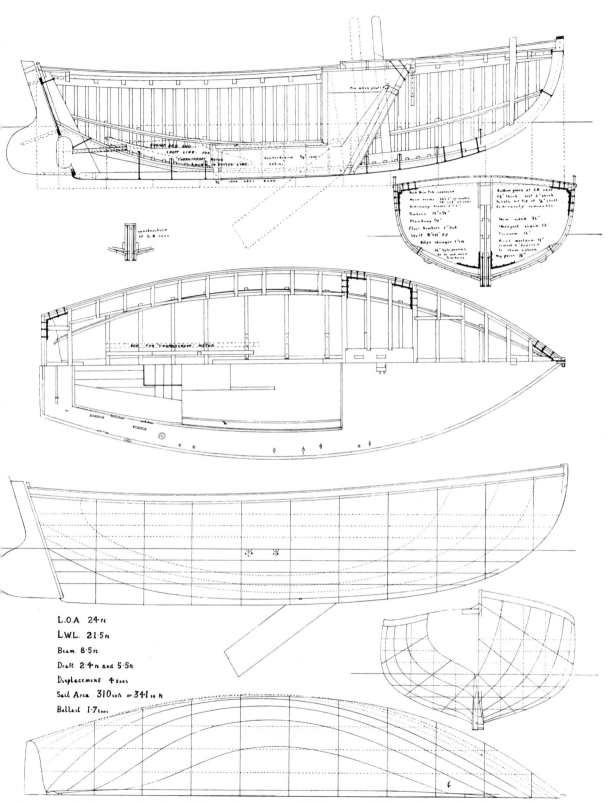

L.O.A 24 ft
LWL. 21·5 ft
Beam 8·5 ft
Draft 2·4 ft and 5·5 ft
Displacement 4 tons
Sail Area 310 sq ft or 341 sq ft
Ballast 1·7 tons

Norma's construction plan shows the ' L ' type of centreplate.   With her flat midship section she sits upright on soft ground.

10—LOON, 9 Tons

LOA - - 30 ft.
LWL - - 26 ft.
Beam - - 9 ft.
Draught - 2 ft. 9 in. (C.P. up)
6 ft. (C.P. down)
Displacement 5·35 tons
Iron keel - 19 cwt.
Inside lead - 1 ton
Sail area - 445 sq. ft.
Power - - Parsons 4 cyl. 10-20
Designer - Maurice Griffiths
Builders - J. N. Miller & Sons, St.
Monance, Fife, 1931
Owner - Mr. A. E. Gregory

Loon

LOON represents one of the author's earlier designs and embodies the 'L' type centreplate with the mast tabernacle through bolted at the after end of the lug case. This form of construction leaves the fore deck clear for the slot in which the top of the centreplate lug works, and it enables the whole installation of both the centreplate case and the tabernacle to be firmly built.

Loon was designed in 1930 and built the following year for her present owner. She was planned to take the sands inside Holy Island off the Northumbrian coast. To prevent lying over too much when on moorings and damaging her bilge when being dropped on the sand at half tide bilge keels, 6 ft. 6 in. long, 6½ in. deep by 2½ in. tapering towards the ends, are bolted outside the bilge stringers. The centreplate case is of simple construction and is scarcely noticeable in the cabin as it protrudes only 6 in. above the cabin sole and the folding table is fixed over the top of it.

The owner had a preference for a Scottish type of stern and *Loon's* pointed stern to a certain extent shows the influence of the Fife. The hull is of very light displacement and in order that she should have as easy a motion as possible, her waterlines were made comparatively fine, while the fine run aft and easy bilges have resulted in giving her a motion when under way quite unlike the ordinary full ended shallow draught boat. The owner has told me that she handles and feels just as though she drew 5 ft. and it is almost impossible to tell from the way she behaves in a breeze that there is not more than 3 ft. of her beneath the surface.

Loon's hull shows an easy run aft.

LOON, 9 TONS

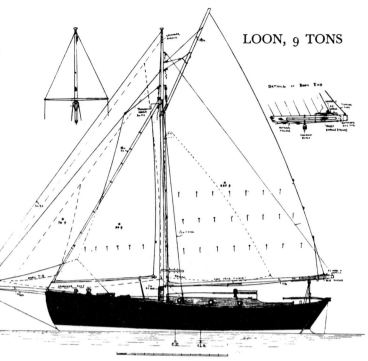

The first engine installed in her, an Ailsa Craig 4 cyl. 10-14 petrol unit, was estimated to give her $5\frac{1}{2}$ knots, but in practice she made $6\frac{1}{4}$. With the present Parsons 10-20 this speed is again slightly increased.

As a fishing and shooting yacht, *Loon* has proved very satisfactory. She has a very large saloon with plenty of space for wet clothes, sea boots and oilskins, and with the coal stove, which is so necessary aboard yachts that cruise out of season in the British Isles, one can be very snug aboard.

With small displacement the snug rig of 445 sq. ft. is enough for ordinary cruising.

With her mast well aft the tabernacle is bolted to the after end of the centre-plate lug case.

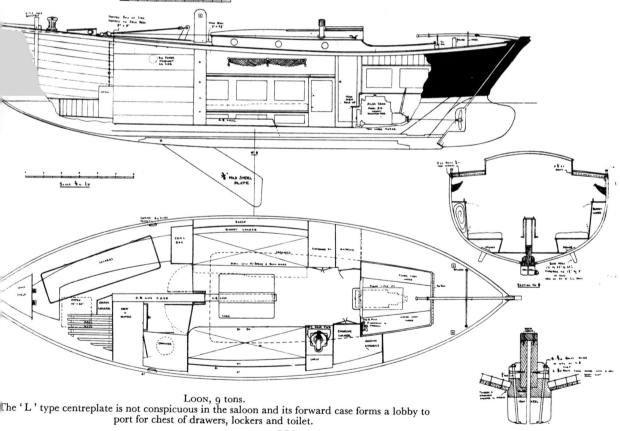

LOON, 9 tons.
The 'L' type centreplate is not conspicuous in the saloon and its forward case forms a lobby to port for chest of drawers, lockers and toilet.

11—AN ALDEN C.B. YAWL

LOA	-	- 45·7 ft.
LWL	-	- 35·75 ft.
Beam	-	- 13 ft.
Draught	-	4 ft. (ex C.B.)
Displacement		32,000 lb.
Iron keel	-	8,840 lb.
Sail area	-	1,050 sq. ft.
Power	-	Gray 4-40
Designer	-	John Alden, Boston, Mass., 1936

MR. JOHN ALDEN of Boston, Mass. (where all the active brains of America seem to congregate !) is known to most yachtsmen in the world as a clever naval architect by his famous line of *Malabar* schooners. Ten of these striking vessels John Alden not only designed but built, each one an improvement on the last, until Number Ten bore but scant relation to the stubby little 41-footer that began the series.

But J. A. has an eye for line and he has designed some remarkably handsome craft apart from his *Malabars*. The Bermudian ketch shown here is a good example of Alden's work in the centreboard line. She is for an Argentine yachtsman who will sail her chiefly up and down the coast of South America and in and out the Plate estuary, where it shoals for miles off shore.

With the aid of the transom berths in the saloon, which stow partly under the berths behind them during the day and can extend to form temporary bunks by night, no fewer than ten people can sleep aboard. The stateroom aft has two double berths, but with the necessarily limited space available for clothes lockers and cupboards, ten would feel something of a crowd for more than one night, I should think. But as any authority on slum clearance schemes will say—backed up, no doubt, by no less an authority than Einstein—overcrowding is entirely a relative term.

With her generous beam and full bilge this yawl should be able to hang on to her three lowers in a breeze until ' things begin to crack ', and with the mizen mast well stepped and well stayed, the mainsail would be the first sail as a rule to be stowed, leaving about 535 sq. ft. of canvas to hang on to. The large single headsail of about 273 sq. ft. is typical American practice. On a full length boom with a topping lift to keep it up when the sail is lowered, it is handled by a four-part purchase sheet leading aft. The lead of the main and mizen sheets is also interesting.

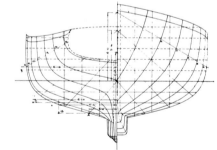

Firm bilges and a good beam.

The centreboard works in a trunk which comes no higher than the level of the table, on which the drop-leaves are hinged. The main companion is off-set to starboard, the cabin trunk becoming narrow at this point to its after end. The trunk also continues forward beyond the mainmast to include the galley and pantry, which is conveniently placed for the crew.

For auxiliary power a Gray 4-40 h.p. petrol engine is installed beneath the bridge deck and drives a Hyde feathering propeller through the stern post.

The area of the three lowers is 1,050 sq. ft.

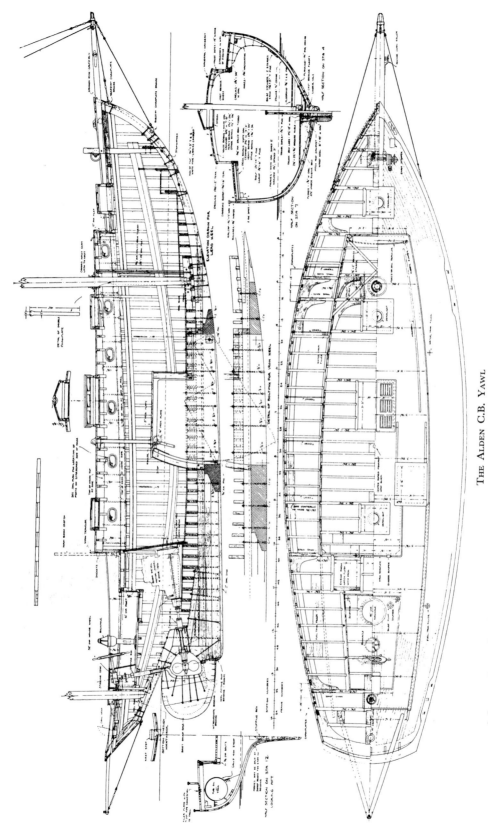

THE ALDEN C.B. YAWL

A fine specimen of an American construction plan in which every detail is given and an elaborate specification becomes unnecessary.

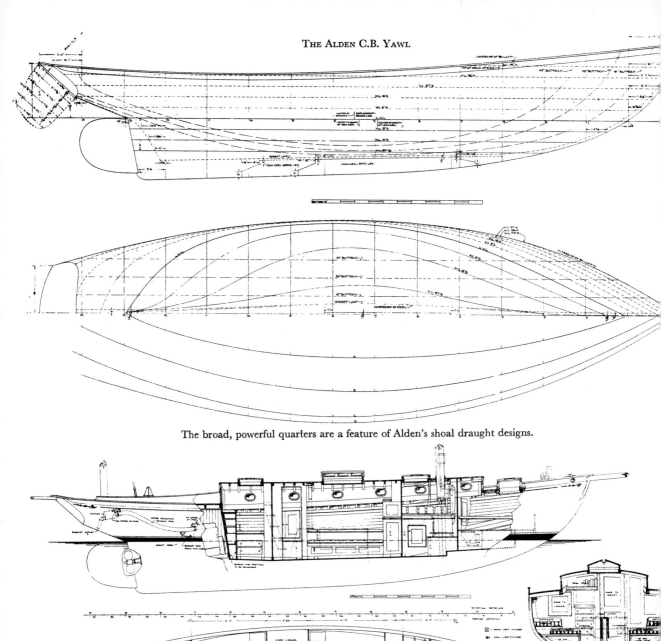

The broad, powerful quarters are a feature of Alden's shoal draught designs.

The layout of this 45 ft. 7 in. yawl will accommodate no fewer than ten people.

12—AYESHA, A FAST C.B. YAWL

LOA - 46 ft.
LWL - 33·2 ft.
Beam - 11·7 ft.
Draught 4·2 ft. (ex. C.B.)
8 ft. (with C.B.)
Sail area 925 sq. ft.
Power - Gray 4-35
Designer P. L. Rhodes
Builders- Henry B. Nevins Inc., City Island,
N.Y., 1932
Owner - Mr. Robert B. Noyes (N.Y.Y.C.)

Ayesha in a 35-mile breeze

IT is not usual for a shoal draught centreboard yacht to make a good showing in the Bermuda Race against the fast deep keel ocean racers that make this one of America's tough sailing events. But, brand new from the Nevins' yard, with her sails and gear unstretched, and a crew of deep keel enthusiasts aboard, *Ayesha* sailed a grand race and took third place in the smaller Class B. And all the boys in her crew became enthused with her fine seagoing qualities and speed. As one report says : ' She had proved not only to handle perfectly at all times, but to be dry and comfortable, with a soft, easy motion in the toughest kind of going. Sea-sickness amongst the crew in the race was noticeable by its absence.'

The lines on the next page show how graceful is her hull. There is a pronounced but not excessive rise to the floor with high, easy bilges (not unlike Geiger's 39-ft. Chesapeake Bay sloop on page 120) and long sweeping buttocks which are cleverly worked into a fairly beamy hull.

All spars of the Bermudian yawl rig are hollow, and with the big Genoa and a sizable mizen staysail, *Ayesha* can carry a lot of light canvas. That she is stiff in a breeze is shown in the photograph taken of her on a run to Edgartown on the N.Y.Y.C. cruise in 1936, when the aerometer aboard *Winsome II* registered from 32 to 45 m.p.h., and *Ayesha* hung on to full sail even in the harder puffs.

As an able and comfortable cruiser for both deep sea and shoal water cruising, *Ayesha* is a credit to her designer and builders. Her graceful hull is double planked with mahogany, fastened with Everdur bronze screws, a sound but expensive form of American construction that is rarely seen in England. The decks and outside fittings are teak and the interior trim is in mahogany with white panelling. A radio direction finder, Kenyon speedometer and log, a Shipmate gas stove and a Gray motor that drives her easily urged hull a good 8 knots, complete her up-to-date equipment.

This is what her present owner writes about her :

' *Ayesha* has always been at or near the head of her class in the cruising division, and that includes all our famous ocean racers. While she is relatively better in light weather, she never in three years' sailing gave me the slightest feeling of instability. She is an excellent sea boat and the best proof of my belief in the type is that I have at present under construction at Nevins an enlarged sister 58 ft. OA, 42 ft. WL, 14·5 ft. beam, 6 ft. draught. Such changes as we have made are slight.

' *Ayesha* is, I think, my twenty-fifth boat ; I have owned both keel and C.B. craft and done much cruising in both kinds. Before owning *Ayesha* I owned for some seven years an Alden keel schooner followed by an Alden keel ketch, both of these excellent boats.

' To my mind all boats are compromises ; what you gain in one way you have to sacrifice in another. Increased size means more draught and this can be met by the proper type of C.B. hull. The dogmatic statements regarding a type by men who have had no real experience with it, is a continual source of surprise to me. Exclusively for racing a deep keel boat is of course somewhat faster to windward than a C.B. boat ; but that is only true regarding the type *Ayesha* represents, *i.e.* the deep type with outside ballast and good deadrise, when you have your sheets pinned in flat on a racing beat to windward. In

115

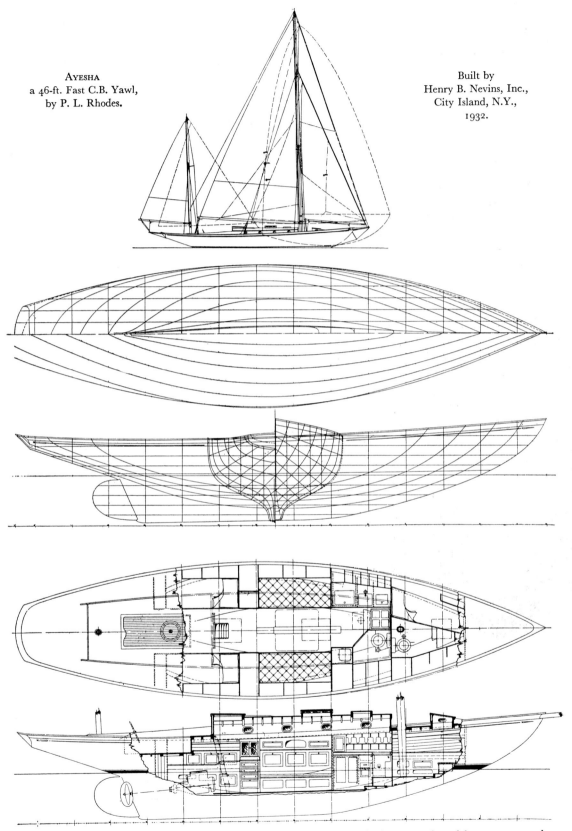

AYESHA
a 46-ft. Fast C.B. Yawl,
by P. L. Rhodes.

Built by
Henry B. Nevins, Inc.,
City Island, N.Y.,
1932.

This lovely yawl has made a good showing in every deep sea race in which she has entered, and her crews come home full of praise of her behaviour. She is capable of a high maximum speed, for with her long balanced ends and sweeping buttock lines, she increases her sailing length by 7 or 8 feet when heeled.

this case the narrower boat can be sheeted flatter and her leaner hull will work out somewhat easier. On the other hand the greater beam of the other boat gives you more room below, and they have an easier motion and are much drier. Their draught allows you to make many harbours that the deeper boat would have to avoid. On my new boat a normal draught would have been at least 2 ft. 6 in. greater and this would have cut me out of some of my favourite anchorages.

'I am not in favour of what you might call the compromise type of keel boat, one of reduced draught in which the lateral area is made up by a longer keel; all those I have sailed in have made what I considered excessive leeway once their sheets were pinned in really flat. I should be interested to learn how *Tiercel* acted under these conditions. While I have not really met any heavy gales with *Ayesha* I am convinced from her performance in ordinary weather she would handle herself as well as could be expected of any boat of her size.'

*   *   *   *

Since the above was written Mr. Noyes has sold *Ayesha* to a yachtsman at Cohasset, where I saw her looking sleek and lovely with her black topsides in the sunshine. To take *Ayesha's* place Mr. P. L. Rhodes designed another centreboard cruiser for Mr. Noyes, a 58 ft. yawl much on the lines of *Ayesha* but with improved accommodation. I spent a most enjoyable afternoon with her owner in Narraganset Bay sailing *Alondra*, and thought her the sweetest thing in yawls that I had ever handled, with her graceful blue hull and tall spars.

She was modern in every way, particularly in her all-wire rigging, winches and well-designed ironwork, and her construction and finish on deck, below decks and, what is more, beneath the teak floorboards, was of such a high standard that I doubt whether it could be exceeded at any South-ampton or Clyde yard: and that, my English and Scottish friends, means the best yards in the country. (The assumption that all Yankee yachts are poorly built is just another of those international myths, like American hustle or eternal fogs in London.)

I am sorry that the plans of *Alondra* were not available in time for inclusion in this volume.

13—A CHESAPEAKE KEEL SCHOONER

LOA - 44 ft. 6 in.
LWL - 32 ft. 6 in.
Beam - 13 ft.
Draught 5 ft.
Sail area 800 sq. ft.
Power - 50 h.p. Gray
Designer Edson B. Schock

CHESAPEAKE Bay is one of those extensive inlets that call for a boat of a light draught, and the owner of this keel schooner limited the draught to 5 ft. Within this limit a boat can enter many of the truly beautiful harbours on both sides of the Bay from which a deep boat is excluded, and the owner of the shallow boat can enjoy many charming anchorages and much peaceful, interesting navigation that his 'long-legged' shipmate must do without.

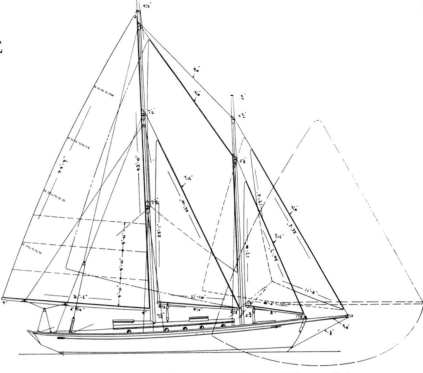

There is 800 sq. ft. of sail in the four lowers of this staysail rig.

When given the order for this design, Mr. Edson B. Schock, naval architect of Los Angeles, Cal., adopted largely the midship section of the old time Chesapeake schooners, giving her a fairly sharp rise in the floor and a high bilge just under the waterline. The bilge has a quick turn to it and in consequence this little ship would not have to heel far before her innate stability came into play. There would be none of that damnable 'sailing on her ear' for a yacht of this section.

A similar body plan was to be found in many of the very fast slaving schooners where an easily driven hull had to be designed with good carrying capacity. As the slaves were all stowed on the lower deck and on shelves close up to the main deck, this called for plenty of beam about the waterline, to form a sharp bottomed hull with a very fine run.

The comparatively light displacement of this little staysail schooner, coupled with her stability, should enable her to make a good showing to windward, although on a long thresh she might—or probably would—be slowly left astern by a deeper craft. But not if the latter happened to be of the heavy displacement, 'one foot in the grave' sort of deep keeler that is just slow anyway.

Under the cabin trunk beams there is 6 ft. headroom and the layout, with berths for five in all, is more or less orthodox American. The great beam gives plenty of space below and it will be seen that ample locker room for clothes and personal gear is available. The short forepeak is used for ship's gear with a locker door opening into the stateroom and a hatch in the deck. Whether—in the case of fire in the after bilge trapping the occupants forward—this door is big enough to allow of egress through the forepeak out to the foredeck, is not clear from the plans, but the possibility is worth considering.

The old slavers sometimes had a body plan like this.

118

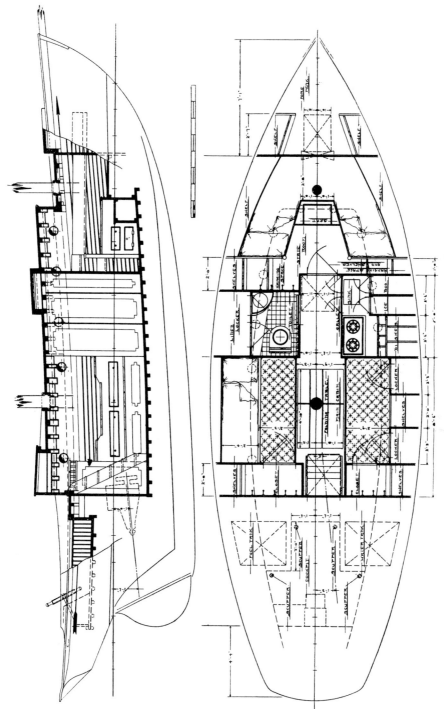

Five can sleep below decks in this 44 ft. 6 in. Schock-designed schooner.

14—A CHESAPEAKE BAY C.B. SLOOP

LOA	-	- 39 ft.
LWL	-	- 31 ft.
Beam	-	- 11 ft. 6 in.
Draught	-	- 4 ft. (ex C.B.)
		7 ft. (with C.B.)
Displacement	-	9·8 tons
Lead keel	-	3·7 tons
Ballast (inside)	-	½ ton
Power	-	- Gray 4-40
Designer	-	- Frederic C. Geiger,
		Philadelphia
Owner	-	- Mr. J. S. Wilford,
		Oxford, Md.

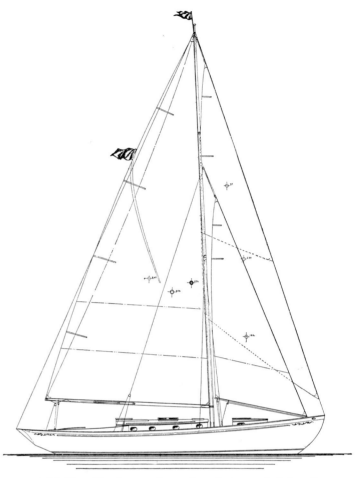

With No. 1 jib of 230 sq. ft. set, the sail plan totals 836 sq. ft.

THE owner of this attractive centreboard sloop requested an easily driven and easily handled auxiliary, which would have a tall rig on which plenty of canvas could be set in the baffling winds that prevail on Chesapeake Bay in the summer, and at the same time would have a really good turn of speed.

This design by Mr. Frederic C. Geiger, naval architect for Yacht Sales and Service Inc. of Philadelphia, is a good example of what can be done within the limits of the above dimensions.

In the lines there is a pronounced deadrise with a very soft bilge at the waterline. Whatever tenderness this form of hull may encourage is set off by the flaring topsides and the generous beam, while both the bow sections and the stern sections have a great deal of buoyancy above the waterline. With her lead keel and ballast totalling some 4 tons, this sloop should behave in heavy weather like a boat of much deeper draught, and I should expect her to handle satisfactorily and to make comparatively good showing to windward even without the centreboard.

Alternative layout plans are shown on the next page, both of them showing berths for four persons. In the case of the plan with the two-berth sleeping cabin forward, there is a small coach roof on the fore deck which gives standing headroom in this compartment. In the saloon there is fully 6 ft. headroom under the beams and sitting headroom under the side decks.

The hull has a very attractive profile with a pleasing sweeping sheer, of which the freeboard is 4 ft. 9 in. at the bow, 3 ft. 2 in. at the stern and 2 ft. 9 in. minimum just forward of the well. These figures include the rail, which tapers from a height of 6 in. forward to 4½ in. at the stern.

The sail plan enables a fine big No. 1 jib of 230 sq. ft. to be carried as a working sail, but in squally weather she would handle under the mainsail and staysail with or without a reef in the former.

The Gray 4-40 has a 2 to 1 reduction gear that turns a 22 in. by 12 in. two bladed feathering propeller, which should give her a speed of about 7 knots.

Details of the centreboard installation in this boat are shown on page 22.

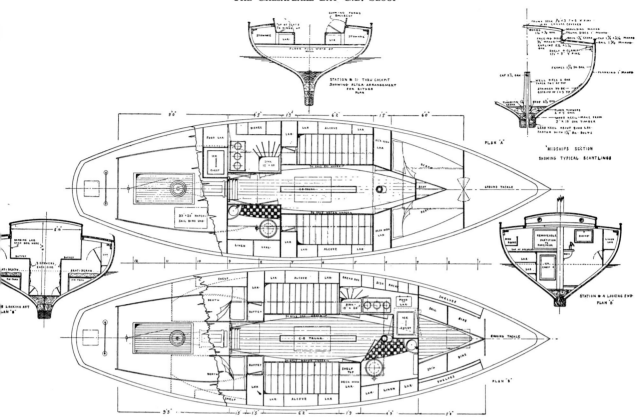

Alternative layout plans (each for four people) enable one to see how well the space in this 39-footer may be apportioned.

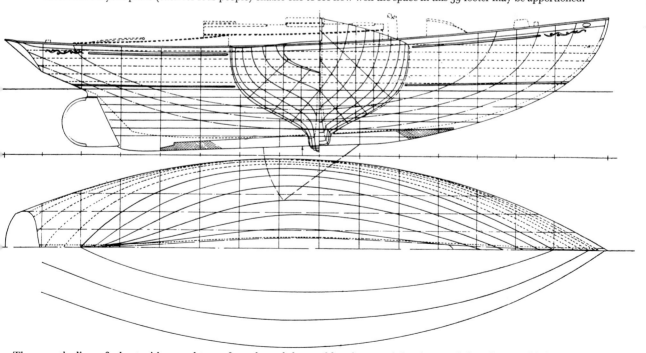

These are the lines of a boat with a good turn of speed—and she would make a good showing to windward even with her board up.

15—SHOAL DRAUGHT FOR LONG ISLAND SOUND

LOA	-	- 33 ft.
LWL	-	- 27·2 ft.
Beam	-	- 11 ft.
Draught	-	3 ft. (ex C.B.)
		6·9 ft. (C.B. down)
Displacement 7·2 tons		
Iron keel	-	1·35 tons
Designer	-	George F. Crouch, New York

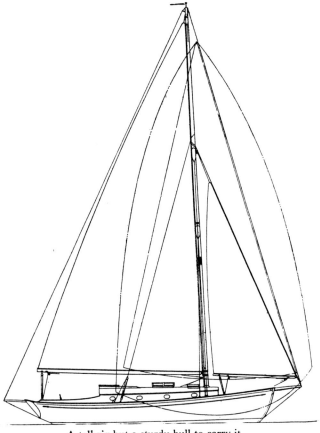

MR. GEORGE F. CROUCH, the chief naval architect of Henry B. Nevins Inc., of Boston, Mass., designed this little cruiser for a New Haven yachtsman who asked for a centreboard boat with a maximum of 3 ft. draught, a really good turn of speed, comfort for four, and seagoing ability that would enable her to face a blow and not come back to be put on the sales list.

Well, here she is ; a trim, stable, sweet-looking hull topped by a tall but handy rig. With her easy sweeping buttock lines and diagonals there is no doubt about her having clean heels

A tall rig but a sturdy hull to carry it.

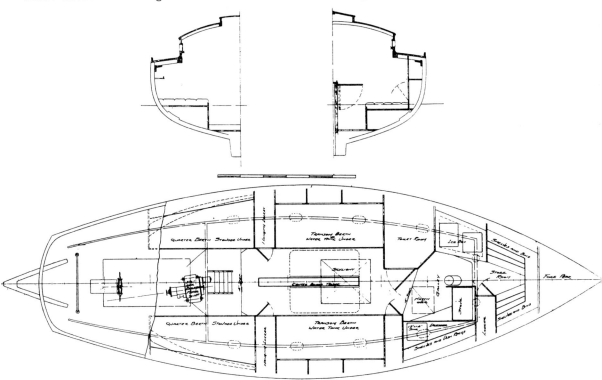

Four can cruise in comfort, even in hot weather.

when she has the breeze abeam or over the quarter. For windward work the centreboard should give her enough lateral plane in addition to that already in her square sided keel to make a good showing on a long tack, and the keel is long enough to keep her fairly steady on her helm.

There is 6 ft. headroom under the cabin top beams and full sitting headroom under the carlines, so that comfort is not ruined by a cricked neck nor a sore head—from beams, anyway.

The galley with its Shipmate range, sink and icebox, is forward around the mast (yes, the mast does look a little too much forward to me. I should have preferred it about 3 ft. further aft) with the toilet room to port, and a useful forepeak for stowage. The usual large self-emptying cockpit and wheel steering of the American cruiser are shown in the plan, with the double outrigger over the counter for the main backstay.

There are many places in the world besides Long Island Sound where a boat of this type would be eminently suitable.

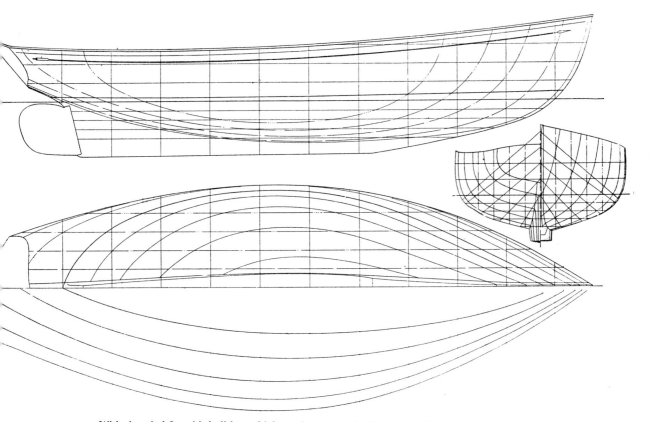

With the wind free this hull has a high maximum speed with ample sail-carrying power.

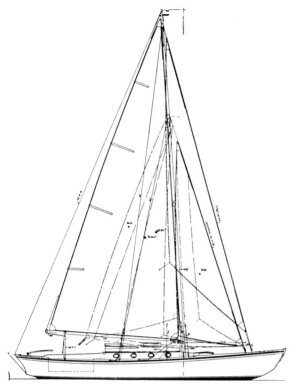

A neat inboard rig of 490 sq. ft.

16—A GERMAN C.B. CRUISER

LOA - - 37 ft.
LWL - - 28 ft.
Beam - - 8·85 ft.
Draught - 3 ft. (ex C.P.)
        5·6 ft. (with C.P.)
Displacement 4·65 tons
Sail area - 490 sq. ft.
Designer - Artur Tiller, Berlin, 1936

IN Germany the large areas of shallow inland seas that surround the capital, and the popularity of inexpensive boat sailing amongst the people have assisted in the development of many small centreboard craft. Amongst the names of designers of such boats, that of Artur Tiller stands out, for he is a competent yacht architect who has many successful and ingenious designs of cruising and racing yachts, as well as power craft, to his credit.

A good deal of racing is done with boats of the cruiser class, and the possibilities for a high speed inherent in a good light-draught hull—as explained in another chapter—are taken advantage of to the full by the more progressive German designers.

The plans of the 37-ft. *Jollenkreuzer*, which are reproduced here through the courtesy of the Editor of *Die Yacht*, is a good example of the high standard to which shallow-draught yachts have been developed in German waters. Although this boat has a centreplate of a very effective area, it is so well hidden that it would not strike any visitor aboard that the ship had any such fitting at all. The hull is stoutly built of German oak, copper rove to bent frames, and the scantlings are in excess of German Lloyd's. Both the centreplate and its entire casing are of mild steel. The case is formed of a single plate bent over at the top and bolted along its lower edges to the keel. All possibility of dry rot or attack by worm, which is so common in fresh and brackish waters, is thereby eliminated, and a perfectly water-tight installation is obtained.

As the top of the case is so near the water-line, only a small opening is allowed in it for the lanyard to pass through to a worm-geared winch bolted to the bridge deck. No stop bolt, to prevent the plate

A shapely hull with 3 ft. draught. Note the boom crutch and folding tiller.

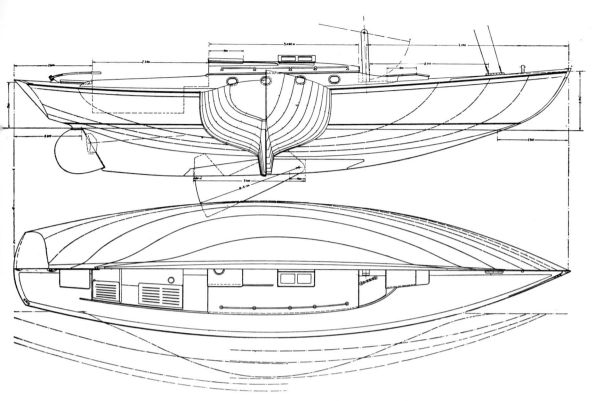

The lines of the 37-ft. *Jollenkreuzer* show a hull capable of standing up well to her canvas and attaining a high maximum speed.

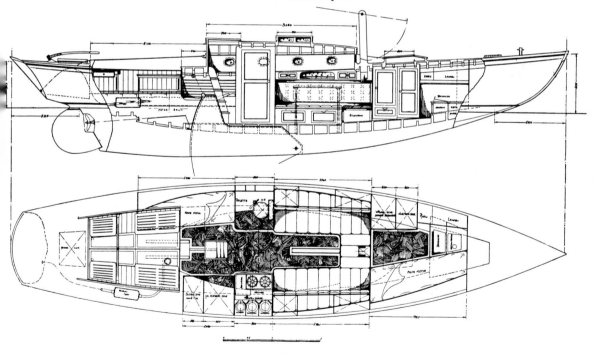

With a port quarter berth four persons can sleep aboard. The centreplate case, which is of iron, is totally concealed below the cabin sole.   Scale 1 : 150.

from dropping right down in the event of the lanyard or its shackle parting, is shown in the plans, but the wisdom of having some safety device to prevent this happening is so obvious that I have no doubt Herr Tiller has allowed for it in the building. A curved slot in the plate and a bolt through the keel, as described in Chapter II, would be one simple way of taking care of this danger.

The *Jollenkreuzer* looks well under way

The position of the centreplate, with its after end out of the way under the bridge deck, brings the leading edge of the plate rather far aft, and this might tend to make the boat 'light-headed' when punching into a steep sea. To have shifted the plate two or three feet forward, however, would have brought the upper part of the case into the centre of the cabin. If, for the sake of balance, this had been necessary, it would then have been advisable to employ one of the other types of centreboards, namely, a modified form of L-type, with the forward part of the case bolted between the partners of the mast tabernacle and the after part of the case hidden beneath the saloon table (as in the design of *Loon*, 9 tons, page 111).

The lines of the hull show a very buoyant bow, almost U-sectioned below the LWL, with a firm turn to the bilges and a particularly clear run aft. The buttock lines are long and graceful, and there is no doubt that this would be a fast boat. With the full forward sections and the generous 'bearing' in the quarters, there is ample buoyancy when the hull is pressed in strong breezes, but at sea I should expect to find that the bow is inclined to pound when driven hard.

Herr Tiller writes: 'This yacht has proved to be uncapsizable during lengthy sea trips, and, with the water-tight cockpit, is also unsinkable. Compared to a heavily-ballasted yacht she has shown an easy motion in a seaway; every sailor who has had an opportunity of trying one of these boats prefers them to keel yachts. The flying jib is the first sail to be handed when it starts to blow. The yacht does not change her trim by having the flying jib removed, and she is particularly smart when tacking in not too heavy a seaway. When running she is well balanced, because of her long fin (keel).'

The rig is orthodox, with alternative cruising and racing headsails indicated on the plan. Two forestays are included, with an arrangement for adjusting their lead on deck. The mast appears tall, to English eyes, to be in a tabernacle, but on the Continent is not in the least an excessive example of a modern lowering mast. It is, of course, a hollow laminated spar.

The layout of the cockpit, with a full-width helmsman's seat, half-length fore and aft seats and a place each side free of seats where one may stand against the coaming, is a good arrangement which I have used in my own boats for some years. The resulting floor space appears far greater than in the more orthodox well with seats running its full length fore and aft.

Below decks this little sloop has 5 ft. 8 in. headroom under the coachroof, sleeping berths for four, a midships galley opposite the enclosed toilet, and ample locker space. The 14 h.p. 4 cylinder motor is installed abaft the centreplate case under the bridge deck, and drives a central propeller, giving a speed of 6½ knots.

To give some idea of the surprising stiffness under sail of this clever design, a set of stability curves,

126

which was worked out by Mr. Henry A. Scheel, an American designer who collaborated with Herr Tiller in this design, is reproduced here. From these diagrams it will be seen that the yacht is still stable, or able to right herself, when pressed over to 90 degrees. As she would recover herself even if given a complete knock-down till her mast was in the water, therefore, she is absolutely uncapsizable.

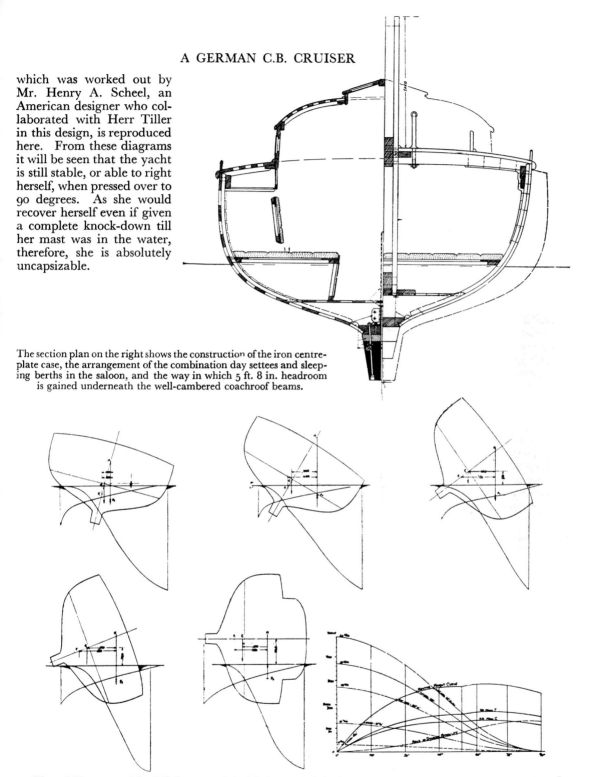

The section plan on the right shows the construction of the iron centre-plate case, the arrangement of the combination day settees and sleeping berths in the saloon, and the way in which 5 ft. 8 in. headroom is gained underneath the well-cambered coachroof beams.

The stability curves of the *Jollenkreuzer* made by Mr. Henry A. Scheel, show her righting moments at various angles to] 90 degrees, when, with her mast and sails on the water, she should still be capable of ' picking up.'

17—A DUTCH CENTRE-
BOARDER

LOA   - 29 ft. 6 in.
LWL   - 27 ft. 9 in.
Beam   - 9 ft. 10 in.
Draught   2 ft. 8 in. (ex C.B.)
          6 ft.   (with C.B.)
Sail area 402 sq. ft.
Designer J. P. G. Thiebout, Zwolle

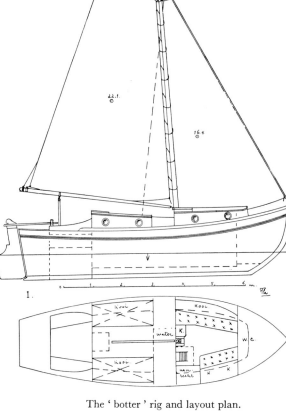

The ' botter ' rig and layout plan.

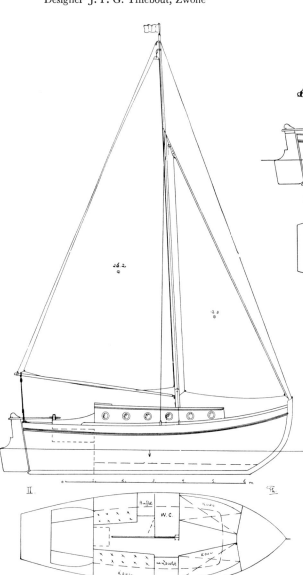

As today's fashion might have it (Scale 1 : 120).

LIKE the seagoing botter, whose influence can be traced in this round-bellied little Lowland sloop, the bow sections are of a shape that graced the sea paintings of Van der Velde the Elder and that helped many a late eighteenth century English revenue cutter to bust her way through the angry seas off the Start. There is little difference between the stem profile that Herr Thiebout shows in his design (for the reproduction of which I am indebted to the Editor of *De Waterkampioen*) and the stem of a cutter yacht of 1750. A little more curve, maybe, above the waterline, and not quite such a bluff bow, but the waterlines forward, the body plan and the fine run aft were all to be found in the speedier cutters of that early date.

The full bow gives plenty of room forward of the mast, which in one plan is devoted to two wide sleeping berths with the saloon aft and toilet between, and in the other has the saloon forward and the sleeping cabin aft. The gaff sloop rig is typical of the ordinary botter with its narrow loose-footed mainsail and big foresail, but one misses the familiar and attractive curved gaff.

Of the more modern alternative Bermudian rig the designer writes :

' The Bermuda rig shown is, to my idea, *not* suited for a cruiser of this kind, but I gave it because many people will not even look at a boat with a gaff rig. The Botter rig has many advantages : the mast, balanced by lead, lowers easily, the absence of shrouds enables one to use the botter (Genoa) foresail permanently. In a squall this is lowered and with the centreboard raised a little the boat handles well with the mainsail only. I am convinced that this botter rig will be faster.'

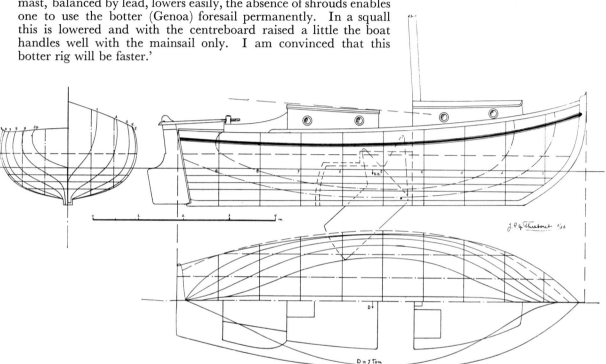

Lines of Herr Thiebout's ' botter ' centreboarder (Scale : 1:80). The wooden centreboard is shown.

So much, then, for fashion. Certainly the Bermudian rig would be very ineffective aboard a short hull of this one's displacement. But there will always be yachtsmen who cannot see why that is so, and why a rig that is admirable and efficient for an easy lined, light displacement hull becomes inadequate and unsuitable for a bluff, full-lined, heavy hull.

There are boats in Portugal today of from 30 ft. to 50 ft. trading in and out of Lisbon that are strikingly similar to this sloop. It is true they have no centreboards, but they sometimes rig temporary and very ramshackle-looking leeboards. Showing the influence of Dutch settlers, these Tagus barges (or boukes) are rigged with stem head foresails and narrow mainsails with short straight gaffs, just like this design, but in their case the mast rakes sharply aft about 15 degrees, and the mainsail is boomless. I have sailed against a number of them, and when light or only partly loaded they leave a clean wake and make a surprising speed, but they are mighty slow to windward. And what is an added attraction when one sees a fleet of them turning up to Barreiro or Alcachete, is that they are nearly all ornamented with bright colours. The Portuguese are fine sailormen and it is a joy to see these vividly coloured barges, with perhaps a sprinkling of lateen-rigged boats of Mediterranean origin amongst them, tacking and cross tacking on the strong flood past the tower of Belem whence Vasco da Gama left on his epic voyage.

18—IONIA, 29 TONS

A Bachelor's Cruising Home

LOA -	- 45 ft. 6 in.
LWL -	- 39 ft.
Beam -	- 13 ft.
Draught -	3 ft. 6 in. (ex C.B.)
	8 ft. (with C.B.)
Displacement	15·7 tons
Iron keel	· 3·75 tons
Sail area	- 1062 sq. ft.
Designer	- Maurice Griffiths
Builders	- Ahmed Gomah, Alexandria, 1933
Owner	- Mr. Colin A. Marshall

WHEN contemplating a cruising life afloat when the time should come to retire from a bank in Alexandria, Mr. Colin Marshall, Commodore of the Royal Yacht Club of Egypt, noticed the plans of the 30-footer *Loon*, and requested me to design him a boat on fairly similar lines with a fixed draught not exceeding 3 ft. 6 in., which would be able to face any kind of weather that she may run up against in winter and summer cruising around the Mediterranean.

As I have stated elsewhere in this book, the fact that the draught is limited to something like one third of the beam need not necessarily detract from a yacht's sea keeping qualities, and now that Mr. Colin Marshall has cruised many hundreds of miles in the Mediterranean and come through all sorts of weather, I am glad to say that *Ionia* has proved capable of living through any weather one is likely to meet in that part of the world.

To a certain extent her hull resembles that of Mr. Henry Howard's *Alice*, which has proved one of the most successful centreboard cruisers afloat, and as in *Alice* the cabin top is extended to the sides with a break in the deck just abaft the mainmast and just forward of the bridge deck. This can be clearly seen in a photograph of the deck.

The centreboard is of oak weighted with a 150-lb. cast iron shoe, and I understand it has given no trouble. The case is continued to the deck and forms a fore and aft bulkhead between the lavatory and double berth cabin to port and galley and single berth cabin to starboard. To allow for hot weather all ports open and both skylights are square and removable so that they can be placed to open fore and aft if desired.

It was originally intended to fit a 14 h.p. Diesel engine, but although *Ionia* has been afloat now for four years, no engine has yet been fitted. Her hull is so easily driven and handy that she can be sailed and manoeuvred if there is the slightest air and her owner states that she hardly ever needs power.

She was stoutly built at Alexandria of selected wood with grown acacia frames. The fact that primitive tools, of the kind that built Cleopatra's fleet, were used in her construction has not prevented her from being soundly constructed with a finish equal to that of most modern yachts.

I think *Ionia* is a fair example of what can be done in a shallow draught hull which is intended for deep sea cruising.

Plenty of deck space.

130

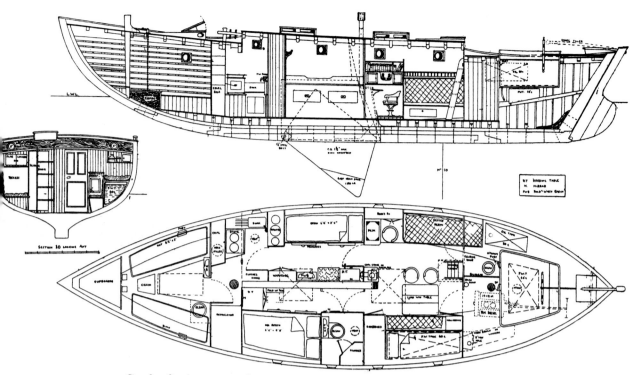

Comfort for the owner and one or two guests, and two Arab hands forward.

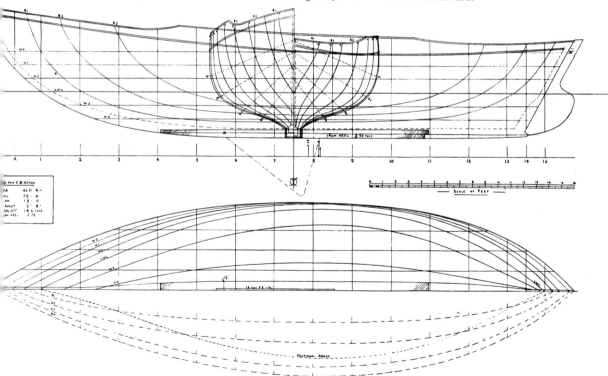

Ionia has a 'saucy head.'   Like *Loon* (9 tons) her lines are easy, and although steered by a tiller a tackle is never needed.

131

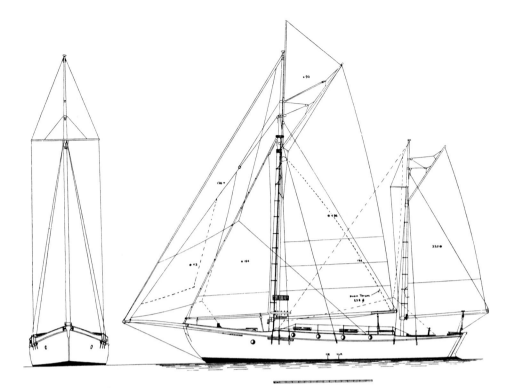

Ionia can set a number of kites for light weather, totalling 1384 sq. ft.

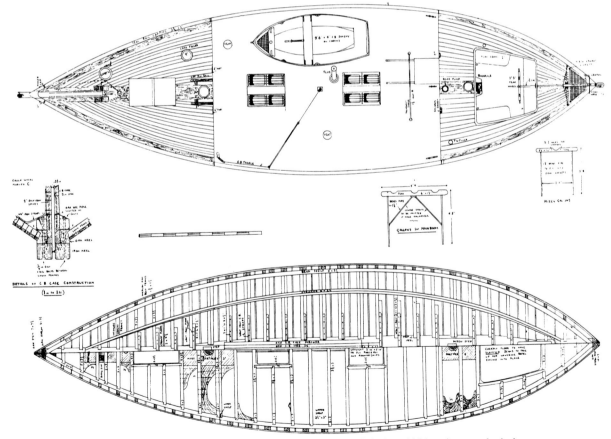

The hull is built chiefly of acacia with grown frames. The raised deck amidships gives ample deck space.

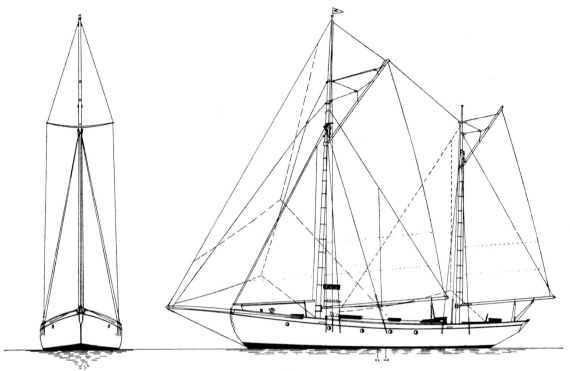

None of the sails is big enough to cause much trouble when short-handed.

19—SUNQUEST, 30 TONS

A Seagoing Home for the Mediterranean

LOA	- 50 ft.	Beam -	- 13·5 ft.	Iron keel	- 7 tons
LBP	- 44·25 ft.	Draught	- 5·5 ft.	Designer	- Maurice Griffiths
LWL	- 40 ft.	Displacement 20·4 tons			

*S*UNQUEST was designed specially to meet the needs of a yachtsman in Egypt who wanted a good healthy cruiser in which he and his wife could live almost permanently with fair comfort ; which they could handle with the aid of one paid hand (a good Arab sailor) up and down the Mediterranean, and yet take over shallow bars when necessary. The draught was strictly limited to 5 ft. 6 in. and, being an Englishman, my client said ' Fixed keel, please. No centreboard.'

It was unfortunate that other plans for living had to be made when the design was completed, and the order for building was never placed, for I think this would have turned out a successful seagoing home of her kind.

The gaff ketch rig had been chosen in preference to the Bermudian, although I should prefer to have rigged her as a jib-headed ketch with perhaps 10 ft. added to the mainmast and some 6 ft. to the mizen. It would have made her better to windward, for the mizen in a gaff rig sags away badly to leeward, and the main is not much better, even though a vang from the mizen masthead to some extent takes care of this tendency to sag.

To ensure ample air space and light below, the deck amidships is raised to the level of the bulwarks (the deck plan shows this). For air in hot weather the after skylight is square and made to lift off and open athwartships when desired. Several features of *Ionia's*, indeed, were incorporated.

The main saloon is about 10 ft. by 12 ft. and has an owner's writing desk, swivel chairs and an anthracite stove for winter cruising. The galley is on the wrong side and should have been to port

133

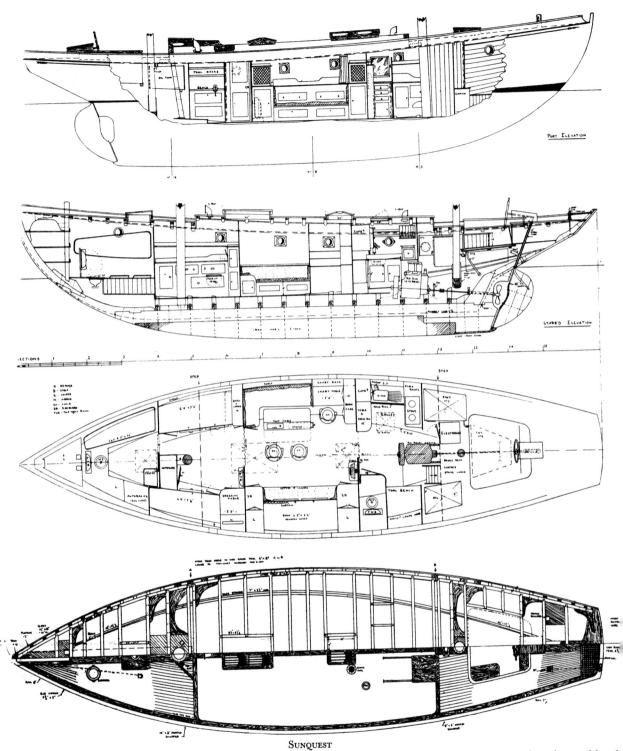

SUNQUEST

As a shoal-draught home afloat this 50 ft. keel ketch has all the space and comfort needed by an adventurous couple and a good hand
She ought to be 'man enough' to go anywhere in the world—and places from which 8-ft. draught would be barred.

with the toilet, work bench and main companion to starboard. (I cannot recall why this was laid out like that. The galley is always best on the lee side when the ship is left to look after herself, hove-to on the starboard tack.) The Diesel engine would—or should in my opinion—be covered over with some sound-proof material which can be easily removed : for this class of engine generally makes a tiresome racket in a confined space like a small boat's engineroom.

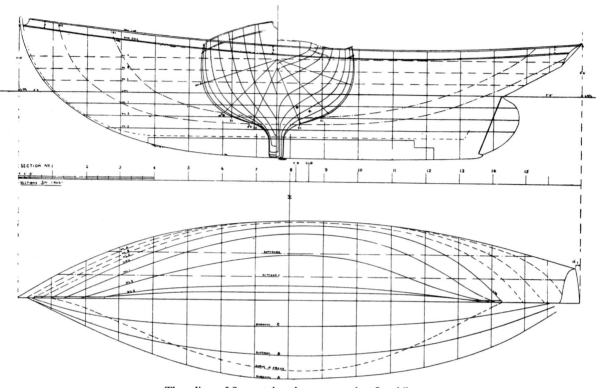

These lines of *Sunquest* show her easy run but firm bilges.

A somewhat easy bow and run aft are combined with firm bilges which give floorspace below and stability. I think *Sunquest* would have enough lateral plane to go to windward satisfactorily, and I hope that the owner will even yet realize his ambition to build her.

20—AYUTHIA, 20 TONS

All-Teak-Built C.B. Ketch

LOA - - - 45 ft.
LWL - - - 36 ft.
Beam - - - 11·6 ft.
Draught - - 3·5 ft. (ex C.P.)
            6 ft. (C.P. down)
Displacement 13·2 tons
Iron keel - - 4 tons
Power - - - 14 h.p. 2 cyl. Diesel
Sail area - - 835 sq. ft.
Designer - - Maurice Griffiths
Owner - - Mr. E. D. Atkins
Built - - - At Bangkok, Siam, 1936

Ayuthia

DESIGNED expressly to be built by native labour at Bangkok almost entirely of local teak, and to be suitable for cruising in the shallow estuaries along the coast of the Malay Peninsula and, later, through French waterways, *Ayuthia's* draught was strictly limited and a centreplate agreed to.

Like *Sunquest* she was to be used largely as a home afloat by the owner, who asked for the gaff ketch rig, but she was to be a singlehander as no crew would be carried. Like *Sunquest* again, she has the stateroom forward and a large saloon with anthracite stove, writing desk, at least one comfortable chair and plenty of floor space.

With her firm bilges *Ayuthia* is very stiff and hangs on to her canvas in a breeze. In one violent squall, the owner tells me, she was knocked down till the water was up to the skylight, but righted herself, so one may say that despite her small draught she is a stable little ship, and her owner is enthusiastic.

Her building was an event of some interest and only the best teak from the surrounding plantation went into her hull—even the keel was of teak, and the transom was sawn from the biggest piece of teak ever known in the district. I guess *Ayuthia* will outlast any of us.

With the polished teak panelling, selected for its grain, the interior is a comfortable little home to be proud of, while it is not sadly cut

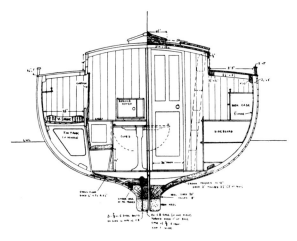

Section through saloon looking aft.

up by the centreplate case which, as the plans show, forms only a short fore and aft bulkhead by the galley. The entire case is of galvanized iron, riveted and bolted to the teak keel with a leak-proof joint. For working the plate—which is of ½ in. mild steel—a winch is bolted to the after coaming of the cabin top and in reach of the cockpit.

After cruising around Malayan waters *Ayuthia* was shipped to England and is now, I believe, cruising on the East Coast, where she is perfectly suited to local conditions.

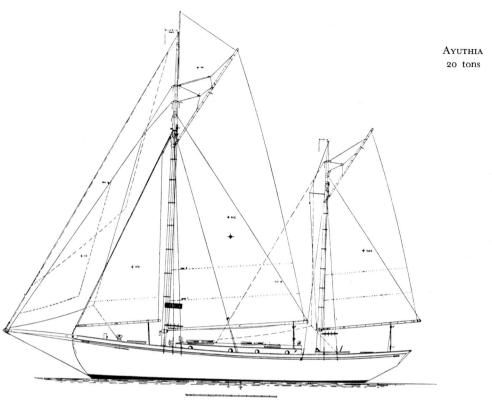

Her cruising rig has 835 sq. ft. in the four lowers.

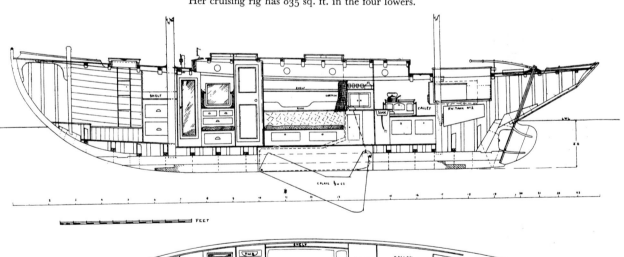

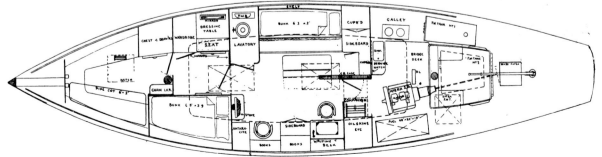

The layout was planned for owner-and-wife cruising with an emergency berth in the saloon and a cot in forecastle.

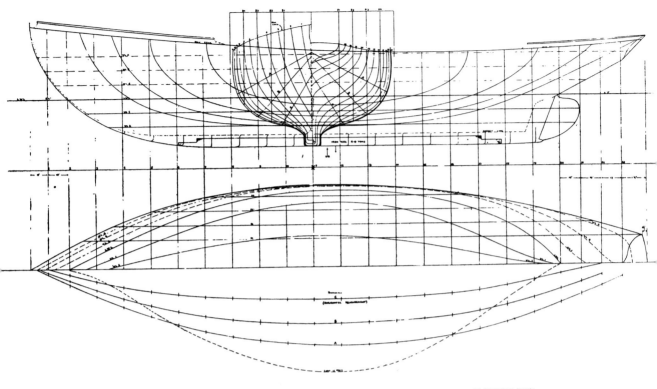

AYUTHIA, 20 tons

The lines show the easy bow sections, the run aft and the comparatively flat floor. (Scale 1:80).

Details of the galvanized iron centreplate case. The sides are in one piece and are carried down through keel slot and bolted to underside of iron keel. The top is bolted on, but removable if necessary.

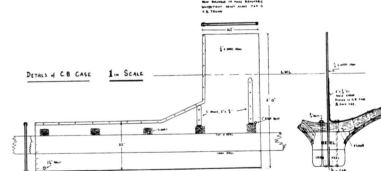

DETAILS of C.B. CASE   1 IN SCALE

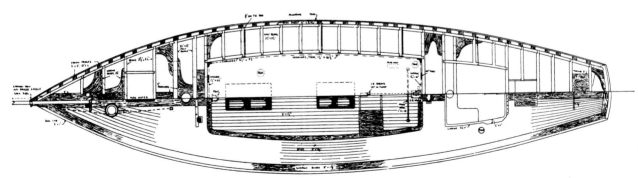

The deck plan shows the beam construction. (Scale 1:90).

138

21—A STANDARD CHINE 40-FOOTER

LOA   - 40 ft.
LWL   - 33·5 ft.
Beam   : 11 ft.
Draught 3 ft. 3 in. (ex C.B.)
        7 ft.   (with C.B.)
Designer David Hillyard
Builder - Hillyard, Littlehampton, Sussex

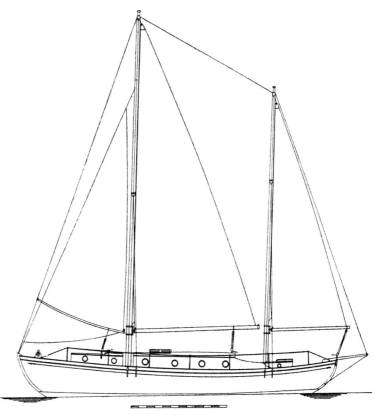

The sail plan, showing divided boom foresail.

TO English yachtsmen Mr. David Hillyard's cheery personality and infectious enthusiasm are associated with the first successful production of standard yachts in this country. It was back in 1922 that Mr. Hillyard began to build little 20 ft. sloops as a standard job, using the same moulds and patterns for many others. Now at his Littlehampton yard, where the placid Arun flows out into the English Channel between two long piers, there are nearly a dozen different types and sizes of boats each of which is built as a standard production. In the past thirteen years, Mr. Hillyard told me, he has turned out some 300 craft and all but a few exceptions between 3 and 20 tons.

For some years Mr. Hillyard has been conscious of the demand for a good shoal draught cruiser with a seagoing hull that would make any reasonable coastal passage, and the latest additions to the fleet of 'standards' are three chine-built (or dead-rise) craft with centreplates or boards, 24 ft., 30 ft., and 40 ft. LOA.

The 40-footer, whose plans are reproduced here, is a particularly shapely craft afloat; and the

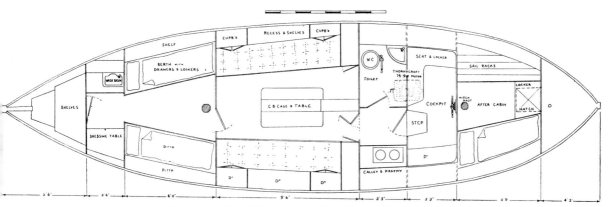

The layout plan of the standard Hillyard 40-ft. C.B. ketch.

angle of her chine scarcely shows above the water forward or aft. The body plan reveals her good, buoyant sections and nice flaring topsides, giving stability and 'lift' when pressed over, and the pecked line across the body plan indicates where she floats when sailing fairly hard.

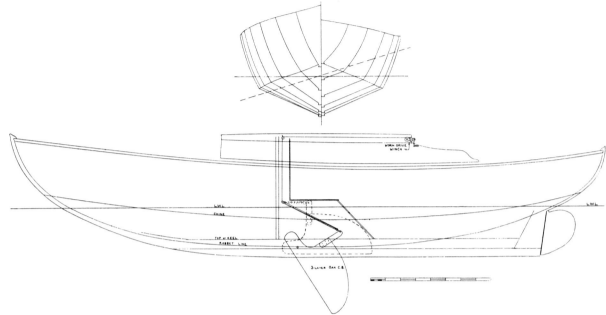

Body plan and C.B. installation of the Hillyard 40-footer.

The centreboard (Mr. Hillyard is trying both oak boards and galvanized steel plates and finds the former much better to handle in practice) is a neat installation, as the elevation shows, and is worked by a worm-driven winch in the cockpit.

These boats, ketch or schooner rigged, with the layout below decks shown, are built for around £800 including all sailing gear and a $7\frac{1}{2}$-9 h.p. Thornycroft engine.

22—BUTTERCUP, WITH BILGE KEELS

A New Version of Shoal Draught

LOA	-	25 ft.
LWL	-	22 ft.
Beam	-	7 ft. 2 in.
Draught	-	2 ft. 6 in.
Displacement	-	2·5 tons
Sail area	-	270 sq. ft.
Thames Tonnage		4½
Designer	-	Robert Clark
Builders	-	Rowhedge Ironworks, Essex, England, 1937
Owner	-	Mr. Charles E. Foster, J.P.

Buttercup sails well

WHEN you feel you need a boat that will always sit upright on either hard or soft ground, you have to do something drastic about it ; for the conventional yacht will not sit bolt upright on a hard shore, nor even the ordinary centreboard craft with any sort of keel. The barge yacht will, but maybe you don't like the cowlike angularity of a barge or a skipjack.

Mr. Charles E. Foster, J.P., had other ideas. Why not, he asked, have a shallow hull with two bilge keels on which the yacht sits as upright as a four-legged table ? The idea had been put into practice back in 1928 (and probably a few centuries before that, because I've never yet met a ' new ' idea for boats that hadn't been invented and dropped many years before) by the Hon. (then plain Mr.) R. A. Balfour, who designed and built *Bluebird*, a 25-ft. bilge keel yacht in which he cruised quite extensively around the North and West coasts of Scotland and England. (If you scarcely believe this you will find the boat described in *The Yachting Monthly* for June 1929.)

Wanting not only a little singlehanded cruiser in which he could potter about the Essex creeks and be sure of sitting comfortably vertical when the mud or the sandbanks stopped him, Mr. Foster wanted the boat also to be both uncapsizable and unsinkable. You see, he aimed for mental as well as physical equilibrium when afloat. An idea like that required fostering and Mr. Robert Clark, a London naval architect young enough not to have become hide-bound in his profession, was called in and Mr. Foster's preliminary plans and requirements laid before him.

The design you see here was the ultimate result and it is one of the cleverest pieces of work in yacht designing that I know. And what is more, the little boat is entirely successful. She sails very well indeed, feeling and handling just like a normal U-sectioned racer with a bulb-fin keel. But her righting moments are such that, at least on paper, she cannot capsize, and with the ends of her queer hull filled with Onazote, an extremely light buoyancy material made from expanded rubber, she will not sink if she ever filled up. What more could you want ?

The hull construction, two layers of mahogany over American elm stringers and light sawn frames, is like that of a dirigible—but of course that was not so that the boat could fly if desired as well.

The two lead bilge keels and the short lead skeg keel aft, together with the rudder, are all carefully streamlined. Like the leeboards of the Dutch hoogaarts which lie out at an angle, the lee bilge keel of *Buttercup* becomes most effective when she is heeled until it lies vertical in the water.

Below decks the accommodation with 4 ft. headroom is necessarily plain but enough, as the owner says, for an ' old man with simple tastes.'

The auxiliary engine is composed of a 4 h.p. Britannia outboard motor power head installed below

141

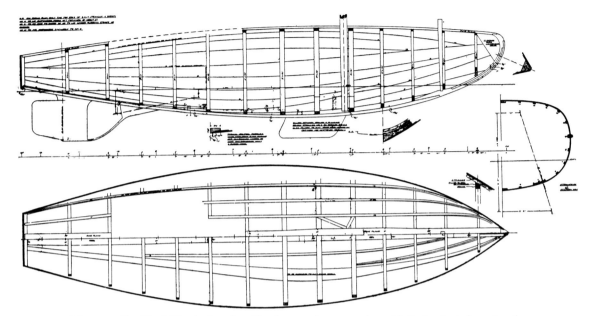

The streamlined lead bilge keels and rudder skeg are shown together with the laminated construction.

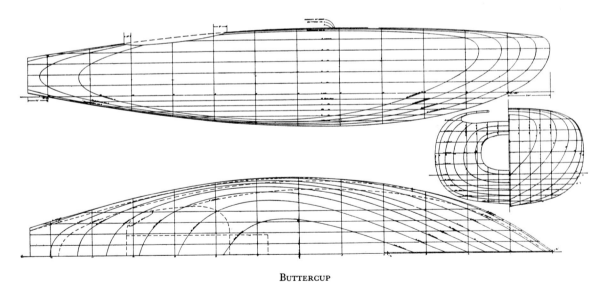

BUTTERCUP

Believe it or not—she sails very well indeed.

142

the cockpit floor, which drives a reversible Stuart Turner propeller through a bevel gear and orthodox central shaft, giving the ship a speed of about 4 knots.

And the name ? Gilbert & Sullivan gave us H.M.S. *Pinafore* aboard which ship ' everything was done the wrong way round.' That appeared ideal, but another yacht already bore the name. Still, there was a young lady in the same opera who had a way with the tars, and she bore an equally good one:

> They call me their Buttercup
> Dear little Buttercup
> Though I could never tell why . . .

Nice as the name is I cannot help suggesting that an even more appropriate one, since this boat is a ' Foster-Clark's ' production, would have been *Mock Turtle* !

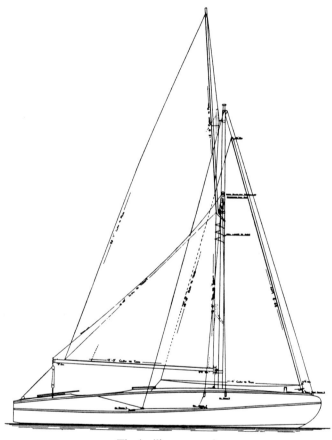

The ' sailing sausage '.

AND NOW MEET SOME OF THE DESIGNERS . . . .

Edson B. Schock, designer
of the Chesapeake Bay
schooner. [P. 115]

Frederic A. Fenger, advocate of the Dhow hull and
maintrysail rig. [P. 103]

J. P. G. Thiebout, designs
shallow Dutch cruisers.
[P. 128]

E. P. Hart, designer of *Windflower,
Har Jeff*, etc. [P. 83]

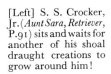

Charles G. MacGregor, designer of
the 26-ft. C.B. Sloop. [P. 88]

[Centre] The Author
aboard *Wild Lone II*
just before she was sold
to make way for a new
28 ft. C.B. cruiser.

[Left] S. S. Crocker,
Jr.(*Aunt Sara, Retriever*,
P.91) sits and waits for
another of his shoal
draught creations to
grow around him!

PART THREE
Under Way

Rawanah was a fine boat at sea.

The anchorage inside Puilladobhrain.

A Cruise to the Hebrides

'As soon as we get aboard we'll up anchor and clear out. It's a foul anchorage in weather like this.'

My host and skipper must have noticed the look I gave him.

'Get anything to eat on the train?'

I had the impulse to tell him just what I thought of Glasgow at seven o'clock of a cold, rainy morning, after an all night journey from a London office; I ached to unburden myself about a train without a breakfast car that had detoured over half the rugged Highlands to avoid a landslide on its ordinary line to Oban. And now it was after 2 p.m. and the salt spray was being dashed over us as the hired launch hurried us across the bay that would have swamped *Rawanah's* pram dinghy.

The grey town, spreading around the bay and crowned with its roofless mausoleum that stands on the hill above as a monument to some madman's folly, began to fade in the mist astern, while ahead of us the outline of Kerrera Island loomed in lumps of rain-washed rock. Oban, the Gateway to the Lochs, looked wet and cold and deserted.

'We've had it warm and sunny up here the last week,' H. A. shouted in my ear as though apologising for the Highland reception.

147

I turned my coat collar higher and took in a deep breath of salt spray. Never mind, it tasted good with the tang of the Atlantic behind it and I felt a surge of excitement as we rounded-to under *Rawanah*'s stern.

There was a clatter of halyards and the sting of spray as we ranged alongside the ketch's grey topsides and clambered over her rail. But below decks it was warm and quiet with the cheerful glow of the coal stove to greet us, and my skipper—I think of him always as H. A.—grinned as he produced a bottle of Guinness and some appetising biscuits.

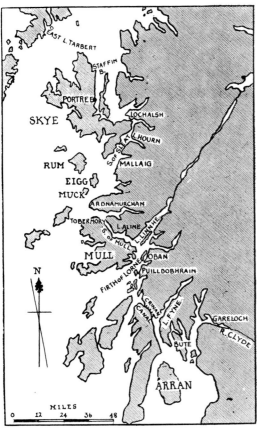

The West Coast of Scotland.

'Will that keep you quiet till we make Loch Aline for the night—it's only two hours' sail?'

Then he clambered on deck again, leaving little pools where he had stood in his oilskins; and while I changed and stowed my shore kit in the fo'c'sle locker, and felt the warmth radiating from the precious Dublin milk, the thud of sea-boots and the crackle of patent blocks called from on deck. Hurriedly tying the body and soul lashing around my oilskins I joined H. A. at the windlass, while the wind roared under our sou'-westers and the main boom, with the reefed sail set, crashed back and forth, jarring the ship.

'Couldn't get a mooring,' the skipper panted while the pawl punctuated his words with its spasmodic *clink clink clink*. 'Hell of a game anchoring up here. Twelve fathoms!'

We were both panting before Gran'pa, the big anchor, rose, cold and muddy, under the bow. H. A. nodded and I went off to the wheel. Being a good skipper he likes to cat his own anchor, and being the crew I just love to let him. Soon we had the staysail set and with the jib and the mizen still in their lashings *Rawanah* heeled and forged ahead for the northern entrance to the bay.

I had sailed with H. A. before and knew his likes and dislikes. In our different ways we are both rather solitary, preferring to cruise alone to putting up with some uncongenial fellow solely for company. I had known him since he had retired from a long service on a railway in Northern India, and had supervised for him the building of his first new ship, a 30 ft. double-ended ketch to a design by old man John G. Hanna, the Sage of Florida. In *Awara*, H. A. had sailed up from his home at Salcombe to the Clyde the previous summer, and there I had joined him for a cruise in which the defects and limitations of an excessively short, beamy boat with little grip of the water and too snug a rig had been discussed and the essentials of the next new boat planned.

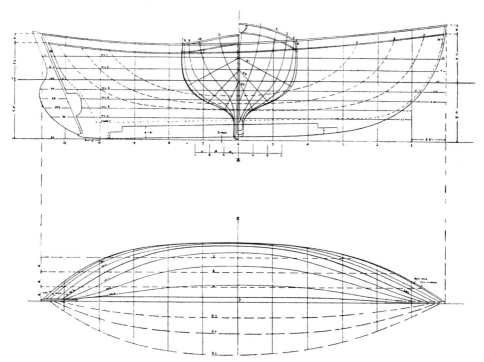

Easy lines to give her a seakindly motion—and a light helm.

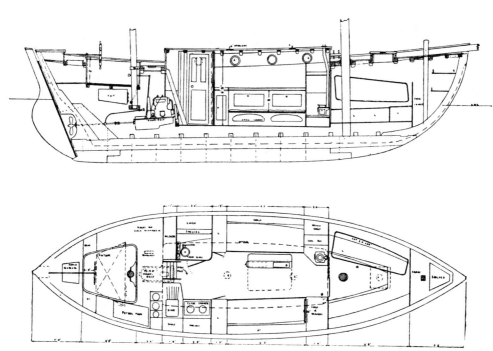

Rawanah's layout was planned for a bachelor to live aboard all the summer.

As the stumpy *Awara* had crashed into the angry seas of Loch Fyne, bouncing and leaping, but reluctant to forge ahead, her owner had said :

' Not.such a full bow, M. G., please, and make her longer on the water line.'

There were other things I had wanted to change, and that autumn the plans of *Rawanah* were drawn up and in due course gave birth to the ship at Pin Mill, in Suffolk, where later my own *Wild Lone II* was to be built.

Designed primarily as a home during the whole of the summer which H. A. could sail alone anywhere he chose around the British Isles, *Rawanah* was simple and open below, with only the fo'c'sle and its cot bulkheaded off. She was 35 ft. OA, 30 ft. WL, 10 ft. beam and 5 ft. draught, and the long straight keel and pronounced forefoot were retained so as to allow her owner to leave her to look after herself while he went below to cook meals, study charts or sleep. Her worm drive steering gear helps, while the rig—a gaff mainsail was insisted upon—enables her to handle under almost any combination. The firm turn to her bilges makes her very stiff indeed and gives plenty of floor space—some 3 ft. 6 in.—and room in the lockers back of the berths.

The 8 in. bulwarks and the self-emptying well with its deep coamings give a good feeling of security on deck, while the easy entrance in the bows and the comparatively fine run aft— for full quarters in a double-ender mean an abrupt upward turn to the buttocks and a slow ship—leave a clean wake. The hull is so balanced that when laid down to the rail in a vicious squall—as far, I believe, as she has ever gone—no more helm is needed to hold her to her course. She steers herself on almost any point of sailing and there never seems to be any fight between the rudder and the ship. 'As H. A. has said, ' The old girl looks after Master,' and on his long passages from Salcombe to the Clyde in the spring and back again before the autumn gales, H. A. has found her as comfortable and easy to handle as a 13-tonner might well be.

Against the hard westerly wind we plunged into the turbulent waters of the Firth of Lorne,

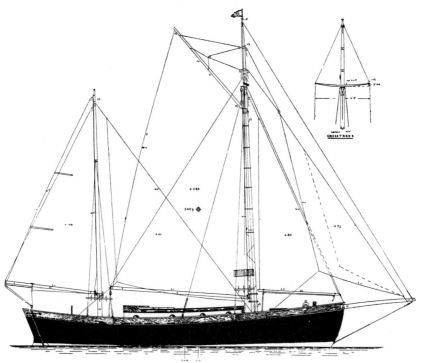

Rawanah is snugly rigged—with 540 sq. ft.—for long distance singlehanded cruising.

while the spray blew away to leeward over the sullen backs of the waves and the water gushed in and out of the lee scuppers.

' Any rocks to loo'ard ? ' I called, peering through the rain. Earlier that day I had been lying in my sleeping berth on the Royal Scot, listening to the rhythmic clatter of the rail joints and the deep-toned wail of the whistle. Now I was gripping the wheel of this sturdy little ketch and threshing to windward through a welter of driven spray and rain. It was an auspicious beginning to a fortnight's holiday.

' Nothing under our lee,' answered the skipper, screwing up his face against the weather. He pointed at the white mark on the end of Lismore island. ' We'll fetch to windward of the Lady Rock. Just keep her full-and-bye, M. G.' Then he went below.

Quite suddenly the rain ceased, and I found I could see up the Sound of Mull as far as the next headland. It was as though a dripping wet curtain had been drawn back, and a pale, cold afternoon sun glinted on the tumbling wave crests. H. A.'s head and shoulders appeared through the main hatch, his pipe crackling, a beret in place of the sou'wester. The lighthouse on the end of Lismore, like a cigarette stump stuck on the rock, was abaft the beam now.

'That's Duart Castle,' remarked the skipper, nodding to windward. 'Looks a grim place to call home, doesn't it ?'

Ah, Duart Castle. A grim, grey, sightless bulwark of pride. I remembered, the last time I was in these parts aboard *Awara* I had gazed on its solid walls wondering what tales it could tell other than of the bombardment during the Rebellion when hot cannon balls buried themselves in the outer wall. The grand old man of the Macleans has died since, but as we threshed past his frowning stronghold that July day he was in residence there, his flag waving proudly to the breeze as it had done those centuries before. And there was no despised Campbell raising his voice in the dim halls now. The Macleans had got back what had always been their own.

Up the broad waters of Loch Linnhe stretching away through our lee rigging three little craft were patiently crawling, their masts like match sticks against the mountains on either side.

H. A. watched them steadily through the glasses.

'They're Norwegians,' he said. 'They're making for Fort William and the Caledonian Canal, on their way home.'

Somehow those three specks, that I knew were in reality Diesel engined ketches of 80 tons or so, gave some credence to the grandeur of the scene, some scale by which one could judge the great distance spread out before us.

And as the clouds rolled back from the peaks of the great rocks, Ben Nevis himself loomed out against the sky, black, frowning, a giant above the heads of his neighbours. But a mist came rolling over the high land ahead, until the very cliffs of Barony Point, like the magic beanstalk, ended in the clouds, and imperceptibly the wind began to lose its weight.

The skipper disappeared below again, only to look out once when I called out 'Lee oh !'

'Want a hand, M. G. ?'

I shook my head and let the old lady come round of her own accord, with the wheel locked to port and the canvas flogging. Then I unlocked the wheel, let it spin round until the rudder streamed, and bent my weight to the lee staysail sheet. Walking forward while the sensible little vessel heeled gently and forged ahead as though she knew exactly how to beat up Mull Sound, I stood for a moment against the weather rigging listening to the moan of the wind in the shrouds and the crash of the bows into the little seas. It seemed good to be able to walk about these roomy decks without having to hold on all the time : it was good to feel the protection of decent bulwarks and to have a ship under one that seemed to know her purpose. It was good, too, to be up here once more, to be able to sail wherever one could see water, to rest one's eyes, strained from the close work of an office, on distant mountains and to be able to see headlands whose shores lay far below the horizon. This was the grandest cruising ground, the most beautiful, this West Coast of Scotland, that could be found in the British Isles, and if only the clouds would blow away and let us see it all . . .

'Tea, M. G. ?'

The skipper, bless his heart, held a steaming mug through the half open main hatch, and I gladly took the plate of bread and jam that accompanied it.

'That's just a stop gap. We'll eat a proper meal when we get into Loch Aline.'

Away to leeward, revealed by flashes of white foam, and showing its flat head above the water, stood the Lady Rock. As I watched it I recalled the oft-told story of how in 1530 a Maclean of Duart, exasperated by his wife's tongue—she was a sister of the Earl of Argyll and a Campbell, and I've always been told those Campbells talked more than was good for them— took her for a nice row in his boat and landed her on this rock. It appears the great lady had more than once attempted the life of her husband, and he had become a little apprehensive, having her around the hearth and the bed chamber all the time. It must be admitted the lady had compensations. For one thing, she wasn't aware that it was the equinoctial tides and at H.W. the whole of the rock, or so Maclean evidently hoped, would be covered ; she was at least spared that worry. And for another, the view from here is one of the most superb in the Highlands. Her relatives, however, had long suspected the Maclean, and before the tide so much as even curbed her tongue, they rescued her—no doubt, as the story omits to tell, to their eventual regret. However, the incident became a popular anecdote in the Highlands and not only resulted in a grim feud between the Campbells and the Macleans, but gave rise to the saying ' Have ye Macleaned your wife this morning ? ' which has since been shamelessly parodied by a well-known brand of toothpaste.

' We can ease the sheets now. She'll make it nicely.'

H. A.'s voice brought me back to *Rawanah* with a start and we pointed our bowsprit at the entrance to Loch Aline.

It looked as though we should be inside the loch in a few minutes. But the time went by and still the entrance stood a long way off with the grim hills rising all round it. I never fail to be misled by the distances in these Scottish sounds and lochs, for the height of the surrounding hills dwarfs everything at sea level and misleads one's estimate of distance. With the seas almost abeam now we rolled and lurched and at last sailed into the smooth water of the loch. The dark masses of hills closed in around us, like sinister demons surrounding a victim, and even the wind, fearful of entering the uncanny maw, deserted us. Gone were the frolicsome waves, the merry hiss and tumble at the bows, the haunting note of the wind in the rigging : we floated, fearful and voiceless ourselves, into the stillness, where the serried ranks of the pines came down to the water's edge and lay inverted on the mirror-like surface.

The burgee girded itself and shook with despair. The mainsheet lifted its parts from the water, while drops fell from it and scattered in rings across the surface, and the little ketch stole quietly past the silent pines.

I looked enquiringly at the skipper, for we seemed to be getting very close to the head of the loch, where the shore came round in a rocky sweep.

' Can you get a sounding ? '

His voice sounded harsh and unreal as it echoed back from the rocks.

I belayed the end of the lead line to a cleat and let it go with a dull splash. The line ran swiftly through my fingers until it tautened with a jerk against the cleat.

' Twelve fathoms and no bottom.'

The skipper peered under the mainsail while I hauled in the dripping line. The ship drifted on.

' Try again, M. G.'

Again the lead plunged down into the cold depths, and the line sang through my hands. It stopped suddenly when a single coil remained on deck.

' And a half—ten.'

' That'll do. We'd better not get nearer the shore.' H. A. clumped forward to the anchor. ' Will you stow the mainsail ? '

The clank of the anchor gear, the heavy splash and the rumble of chain, and the crackle of the halyard blocks echoed from the shore like a sudden burst of musketry. Perhaps, I thought as I clawed the wet canvas, we had awakened the echoes of long ago ; aye, long ago when those fiery Macleans first made their presence felt hereabouts sometime back in the fourteenth century, I believe. Their first act, so it is said, on coming across from Lorn, was to usurp the Mackinnon's land, and in consequence invoked the wrath of the great MacDhonuil-nan-Eilean. A lesser Highland clan might have trembled beneath the anger of the Lord of the Isles and hurried back to Lorn. But not so the Macleans. It would appear that, while the great MacDonald was still rumbling a little inside at these invaders from Lorn, two of the Macleans came to Ardtornish Castle with some innocent-looking proposition concerning the usual question—land. The great lord dismissed them bidding the Mackinnon, his bodyguard, to give the travellers food. But as it was Lent—always a bad time to travel in Scotland—there was no meat for the famished Macleans ; nothing but a bowl of curds and bread, which was mighty difficult to handle on the point of a dirk. And the Mackinnon no doubt was ill-adapted to hide the smiles as the empty Macleans wrestled with the mush.

They say hunger sharpens the wits. Certainly the Macleans felt more than annoyed at being given such poor fare after their long journey and planned some reprisal. When the Macdonald started home in his galley for Mull, they invited themselves aboard the Mackinnon barge and quietly stabbed all its occupants. Those Mackinnon smiles at the Macleans' table manners must have rankled. Then the Macleans caught up with the Macdonalds' galley and in sight of all his castles and within his own domain, they took the Lord of the Isles prisoner. And what is more, they kept the old man prisoner on Garevelloch, a desolate isle, until he had recovered his astonishment together with his speech, and, with Hobson's choice, had made the lands of Mull over to the Maclean clan and sworn eternal friendship. In spite of these professions of faith and love it was not long before everyone was quarrelling with everyone else and the Macleans fighting with the Macdonald of Isla, with their own kin the Macleans of Coll, and with the much hated Campbells who eventually got possession of their Duart stronghold.

All of which seemed to have happened only yesterday as I peered across the water at the shadows under the pine trees, but it had gone so dark suddenly. I had no idea it could be so gloomy long before sunset. Motionless and mysterious the trees, row upon row, stood there with pointed heads like magicians' caps, watching us. Amongst the deeper shadows of their branches, where no eye could penetrate, I felt there were eyes following our every movement, glaring at us for disturbing the stillness of their domain.

Suddenly I stopped tying a gasket and listened. A soft purring sound was coming from the shore. For a moment I could not think what it could be, and then it flashed upon me—*the trees were whispering.* Their heads were nodding together and their grotesque hands stretched out to each other in the gloom of the shadows : some sinister plan was being agreed upon, something that only trees could conjure. And beyond their heads the peaks of the hills rose tall and menacing into the very clouds themselves. The sense of imprisonment stole upon me. I had the feeling that we were caught fast for the night and *Rawanah* would never be seen again...

' My God, M. G., haven't you stowed that mainsail yet ? You'd better hustle, for there's rain coming. Can't you hear it ? '

The skipper's incredulous voice broke the spell, and after finishing on deck I went below, a little crestfallen, to a warm cabin where the soft light of the oil lamps and the ruddy glow of the fire soon played on the blue and white table cloth. And outside night closed in with a downpour of rain that thundered harmlessly on the deck over our heads. But I was done with trees and gloom and creepy sounds and curled up on the port berth with a cheroot and an interesting book while H. A. hustled the radio set.

I can think of no better word than hustled. No programme, however pleasant, lasted more than five minutes. Each was switched on, tried and switched off in turn. I knew H. A.'s little ways and took no notice of the sudden blares of an orchestra, the passing squeal of violins, the bark of a man's voice, the thin shriek of a woman soprano, like a train passing a wayside station, the emasculated *moo* of a crooner, or the precious notes of a B.B.C. announcer while H. A. tried to decide which was the least exasperating programme to listen to.

' I wish, H. A.,' I had once said, ' that I could have allowed space in the design for six radio sets.'

' Six ? ' He screwed up his face.

' Yeah. You'd be able to have all six different programmes going at once. It would save having to twiddle any of those knobs.'

Instead of hitting me he exclaimed :

' I wish I hadn't got the damn thing ! ' and with a click all the tempting noises were cut off and peace reigned. It is curious how peaceful and comforting a quiet smoke and a good book can be after the raucous boom and crackle of an unwanted radio programme.

After the night's rain the morning seemed to be washed and drying in bright sunshine that came down from a clear sky. On deck all was changed. The banks of the little loch—Aline is but a mile or so long and a couple of cables lengths broad—rose tranquil and rocky towards the hills on either side, and the trees were just ordinary pine trees with the sun's rays slanting across their gaunt trunks. On the north side of the loch they were yet in shadow and there was still a sense of gloom where no sun could intrude.

While I took down our riding light, whose flame appeared pale in the sunshine, as though it, too, had been washed by the night rain, I noticed that our anchor cable hung straight down in the dark water, its bright galvanized links turning progressively browner until they disappeared into the still depths far down. A jellyfish, like a transparent celluloid bell the size of a large bucket, drifted slowly past, its own revolting, slimy form tinged with the peaty water. Its long nebulous trailers wrapped themselves around our chain and the thought of others in those very depths dispelled any desire to plunge joyously overboard this morning.

An hour later the exhaust of the Handybilly coughed and spluttered on to the still water as the little ketch nosed her way out into the brighter sunshine of the Sound, leaving astern of her an ever widening wedge of little ripples that spread fanwise across the surface of the loch. The broken skyline of Mull looked grand and inviting in the morning air and the blue waters of the Sound itself faithfully reflected the peaks on the mirrored surface. Far away two white pyramids lay dormant on the water. So small did they seem it was difficult to believe they were two yachts of fair size becalmed somewhere beyond Fuenary Rocks.

Slowly we plugged on, for it was our intention to make for the Outer Hebrides. The skipper, always active, always happy with his own summer home beneath his feet, varnished the forehatch and attended to some frayed ropes' ends and a block that needed a new strop, while I sat harmlessly at the wheel, drinking in the beauty of these Highlands. Truly this West Coast of Scotland is the finest cruising ground of any in the British Isles ; the coasts of Devon and Cornwall, of Kerry and Cork and Co. Down and, for aught I know, of other counties whose beauties I have not seen, may have many attractions for the cruising man ; but for grandeur in scenery, for variety and unlimited snug anchorages, for utter unspoilt, wild loneliness and for its size and area, the West Coast from the Clyde to Cape Wrath as a yachtsman's cruising ground has no equal in Great Britain. But for my own taste, to turn it into Paradise, it needs three alterations (and here I imagine my Scottish reader, or readers, crying : ' Mon, ye'd ruin it ! '). They are : An area, say 100 miles square, given to undulating land and sand dunes with numerous creeks, sandbanks and shallow channels with tricky navigation ; weather less like Scotland and more like—well, better weather ; and thirdly, an even warmer Gulf Stream.

' Och, ye don't appree-ciate it as ye shuid ! '

The hours passed, biscuits and a glass of something or other came, and the narrow entrance to Tobermory Bay from the south between Calve Island and the shore of Mull opened up on our port bow and closed as we passed on. The previous summer in *Awara* we had explored this useful passage into the bay, finding plenty of water at half flood in its clear depths. Yet two local yachtsmen to whom we spoke had never dared try it : the rocks on each side, they exclaimed, ' look so close ! '

As the familiar anchorage came into full view I recalled the story of the young Spanish noblewoman who had become excited by dreaming several times of a handsome fair haired warrior whose home appeared to be in the North. When the Armada gave her the opportunity of a free passage to England she went along in the *Florida* galleon which, after the rout, put into Tobermory. And when Lachlan Maclean of Duart stepped aboard, lo ! it was the hero of her vision, and no mean hero either if one may judge from contemporary accounts and the effect the Macleans have usually had on the once gentle sex.

Of course there was a wife. And the spouse of the Laird of Mull was no lady to go into a decline over a Spanish hussy who had been blown into the Tobermory anchorage and offered her husband abundant hospitality. A little quiet organization, a few faithful followers, and bang ! the *Florida* galleon, with the senorita aboard, blew up with a report that was heard most satisfactorily in Duart Castle itself where no doubt my lady was listening with a certain impatience. And the Spanish menace, or what was left of her, was buried in a stone coffin at Dunstaffnage Castle. I do not know whether Lachlan ever connected his trustful wife with this unexpected termination of what had been literally an amorous windfall, but if, as I suspect, there is not a grain of truth in the whole of this yarn, then it matters not. In passing, however, one may observe that as a method of terminating an over long love affair a barrel of gunpowder certainly has points to recommend it.

A dark line spread across the water from Auliston Point where the headland of Morven swept down into the Sound, and soon we had the brown sails set and the racket of the engine ceased. An entrancing stillness remained while the ship heeled gently, her sails filled out in graceful curves, and the water began to frolic under the lee bow. Tobermory with its grey houses rising terrace upon terrace and overlooking the anchorage where yachts lay facing all ways, passed by, for we had no need to go ashore, and no desire. Several of the boats I recognized and I should have liked to call on two or three of the owners whom I knew, but H. A. avoids a crowd and in any case we wanted to get away north without delay.

The red conical buoy marking the Red Rocks and the junction of Loch Sunart with the Sound of Mull lay like a stub of lipstick far away over the water to starboard, while the cruel rocks showed their gull-whitened heads beyond. As we rounded the frowning headland and caught our first glimpse of the end of Ardnamurchan, the Runa Gall lighthouse stood above our heads like a tall white knight guarding the last of Mull.

And as time went on and the breeze grew fitful with patches of blue calm spreading here and there over the ruffled water, we passed close in to the white guardian of Ardnamurchan, grey outpost for the Western Isles, whose light has been a welcome sight for many a ship in these exposed waters. A long gentle swell, almost imperceptible in itself yet seen against the skyline as a series of undulating hills, was running in towards the land and breaking itself with a continuous crashing roar against the rocks.

' Not a good place to be becalmed, eh, M. G. ? '

I nodded, looking around on the peaceful scene, and thought of the danger that lay in such a swell for a small boat that got too close in to those cruel fangs in calm weather. There had been such a case, a fatal one, but a few weeks before, when a cutter of some 6 tons in the lightest of airs had been rounding one of the outer isles close in to a flat rock that stretched some way under the surface. One of these big Atlantic swells had welled up, carried the cutter bodily towards the point, and then let her crash on to the rock as the water fell, leaving the boat cracked open on her side until the next swell roared up and over her in a turmoil of foam and broken planks and spars. It all happened within three minutes.

One cannot approach these rocks exposed to the ocean with too much caution when the wind is light and the ship has little steerage way.

Away to port, shimmering in the hot stillness, the mounds of Muck, Rum and Eigg, and peeping out from beyond the western point of Rum, the lower mass of Canna, lay like broken puddings on the glassy sea. Rum, like many another island hereabouts, has a tale of hatred and tragedy that is still told. It seems that the Macdonalds, who were in residence—the time being in the sixteenth century—hospitably welcomed some Macleods of Skye who were weatherbound on the island. But when the weather fell calm again the Macleods rather outstayed their welcome, and paid too much attention to the daughters and sisters of the Macdonalds, who were so annoyed that they set the Macleods adrift in their own boat under the handicap of being bound hand and foot. These men were rescued by their kinsmen, and the croakings of the less humane of the Macdonalds who declared that they ought to have stabbed the—

whatever their pet name was—were fully justified later when the Macleod of Macleod landed with a large force to avenge the inconvenience caused his boatmen. The Macdonalds fled to a cave, but footprints in the snow gave them away, and the Macleods followed them and joyfully smoked the entire population of the island to death in their cave. That is why, to this day, children, a Macdonald will never touch smoked fish, as it reminds him so keenly of the ancestral home.

Late that afternoon we let go the second anchor—' Gran'pa ' was too heavy for ordinary use—in the reeking harbour at Mallaig. The necessity to collect mail including charts of the Hebrides sent on from Glasgow had brought us in here ; for H. A. dislikes anchorages with any other boats in them. Railhead of that tricky line from Fort William, Mallaig has all the appearance of the last outpost of civilisation before one leaves for the unexplored north. Alas ! It is not so, there are lots of motor roads, hotels, radios, picture postcards and social amenities around the next headland.

While the drifters, packed like herrings in a box with their proud heads nudging the quay, unloaded their catch, and rawboned, raucous voiced lasses helped the fishy looking men to weigh and pack the silver slipperiness, we kicked our heels until the following afternoon until a tired train brought the charts.

Then our impatience was allowed full rein. The dinghy paddles bent as we frothed across the harbour to the ketch, our wash, believe it or not, rocking the drifters together until they clanged, and within three minutes H. A. was hauling at the winch. His orders barked forth in the voice that had terrified babus in a railroad superintendent's office and changed listless coolie gangs into advertisements for ' Rice for Energy ', and in record time *Rawanah* had spread her wings and sailed away from that smell of rotting fish, oily water and coal smoke that reminds me of Mallaig.

Before us the Sound of Sleat lay sparkling in the evening sunshine, its blue waters flecked here and there with white as the wind swept across the surface. Soon the sun would be hidden behind the great hills of Knoidart, and we decided to look in to Loch Hourn before darkness should find us groping through the tide-swept pass of Kyle Rhea. A sail by day and a calm snug anchorage at night is the rule up here, and with an engine it is always to be obtained.

Like a deep chasm between lofty cliffs, the loch opened out and we sailed into its maw.* Astern of us the broad waters of the Sound frolicked with the lighthouse on the Isle of Ornsay a white chip above the tumbling blue. From ahead a shadow was spreading, darkening the waters of the loch, while overhead a cloud caressed the peak of the land and brought a chill feeling into the air.

Under a sudden fierce blast that pounced down from the hills *Rawanah* heeled until her lee scuppers gurgled and the bow wave rolled over with a hearty roar. Then suddenly she sat upright, her booms swinging in and her sails slatting.

At the wheel H. A. swiftly turned the spokes, his eyes searching the burgee and the water to windward. *Rawanah* sailed on her new course with a fickle breeze. Then a sudden rush of

---

* Its name signifies ' Hell Loch ' and the Admiralty Sailing Directions are more than encouraging about it : ' The squalls come down with fearful violence, and in a few minutes the wind will blow from every point of the compass, lifting the top of the water in a white foam, and twisting it round and round in perfect whirlwinds.'

darkened water flew towards us from the weather beam : the skipper put the wheel over hurriedly and the ship's head slowly rounded-to. Like the blast from a gun the squall hit us and drove the lee deck to the level of the water again. For half a minute perhaps *Rawanah* sailed up the loch with a bone in her teeth, her sheets like iron bars and the mainboom bending.

Then, without warning, she was all aback. The booms swung in once more, the head sheets clattered on the deck and the skipper screwed his face up and glanced past the slatting canvas at the burgee.

Our head swung off once more and we again sailed at right angles to our course up the loch. Time and again this happened : fierce squalls rushed down from the hills and set us aback, then as we got the ship on her course the wind disappeared and left us with boom over-head and the sheets drooping. Sailing into these lochs with their high surrounding hills was always the same. A steady snoring breeze in the open Sound, and then a maddening succession of calms and cats paws, of willie-waws and squalls from all directions. And the closer one worked up to one's chosen anchorage, the more fickle and exasperating was the wind. Two or three hours can easily be spent just working up a few miles to the head of a loch, while a fine breeze flecks the sea outside—unless, of course, you fold your wings and motor instead.

Once again a fine, calm morning greeted us and as the place was so free from interruption —for Loch Hourn has no steamers running into it—and the day the Sabbath, we decided to stay. Not that the Sabbath meant to us so much as it does to certain of the inhabitants of these rugged islands. Only a week previously I had read in a London daily how the elders in one of the islands had refused to allow the kirk's ' privileges ' (whatever they may be) to a member of the crew of a steamer whose regular schedule caused her to sail at 11 o'clock every Sabbath morn, unless he gave up the job. And he did. And the owners of the inter-island line were even requested to desist starting their little steamer on the Sabbath, although the local council had applied for years for this convenient schedule to be instated ! The terror amongst the ignorant and the unnecessary cruelty that advocates of the church have caused from time immemorial is a very black page in the world's history. Men lose all reason, sense of justice, and their pecu-liar acquisition, logic, when some obsession, like a particular religious belief, gets hold of them. Which, to dispel the gloom, reminds me of a truly sad story of an aged professor of English whose obsession was a horror of any sentence that ended with a preposition. In his old age he had a woman read to him every day, and she had to be careful never to finish a remark with a preposition nor choose a book whose grammar was sullied by such a form of sentence. Then one day the old man said : ' I am getting old, Miss Pink. Before I die I should like to have read to me *Lady Chatterley's Lover.*' Miss Pink was so astounded that she blurted out, ' My goodness ! What on earth do you want that book to be read to out of for ? ' The remark was too much for the old fellow, who never recovered from the shock.

No, we stayed anchored in the clean, deep pool, with our bowsprit a stone's throw from the rocky beach because it was sunny and warm, and so far as we could see there was not enough wind even to draw hurrying little finger marks across the surface of the loch. With unheard of energy I glanced up at the peak of Glamachmore that rose 2,500 feet above us and suggested scrambling to the top.

The skipper looked at me as if I had said I was about to drown myself—neither hope nor actual despair, but just incredulous surprise in his expression.

' *Climb*, M. G.? Right up there ? ' From the way he said it the hill seemed to become a mountain at once. ' Not me. But if you'd like to go, and be back in two hours, I'll have a nice hot lunch ready for you. And a Guinness. You'll need it.'

He wouldn't come and, like a perfect host, waived my weak offer to help him enamel the brass porthole rims green—a better shade than their own natural colour. And so to the top of the—er—mountain I went in shorts and a sweater.

' If you don't appear in two hours ', H. A.'s voice had consoled me across the water as I stepped ashore, ' I'll search for you with a flask of brandy—and a gun to put you out of your pain.'

From the summit, against the blue sky the view towards the south-west took one's breath away. The Sound of Sleat lay like a blue ribbon beyond the grim outline of Knoidart, while on the other side the peaks of the Cuchullin Hills in Skye rose in their ever startling shapes against the western sky. In the little bay below, *Rawanah* lay at her anchor like a chip of wood in a pond, and farther up the loch the little valley of the Glen Barrisdale fell away towards the first ' narrows ' in a grand sweep of peaty, boulder strewn wilderness.

Of course there was a higher peak than Glamachmore, a tantalizing black mountain across a half-formed valley, with its proud head obscured by a passing cloud. But there was no time left to climb his rocky sides and I returned to the earth somewhat chilled and aching in the knee muscles, feeling I had really climbed a mountain.

Later that afternoon we motored quietly through the two narrows right up to Kinlochourn, the head of the loch, where we let go in a completely land-locked pool whose sides rose on every hand to 2,000 feet or more. It was calm and peaceful, but all too soon the sun's light was cut off and the whole basin plunged into shadow : soon, too, the blue in the sky above paled and grey clouds began to hover about the heads of the hills and swirl about their faces in trails of chill mist.

Night closed in with a drizzling rain, and an occasional willy-waw shook the halyards, bringing the ship to life, as a slumbering man is half awakened, only to fall asleep again.

The next afternoon found us threshing through the pass of Kyle Rhea on the 6-knot tide where the island of Skye would join the mainland of Cromarty were it not for these narrows. Past the steep shores that closed in upon us only to slip by in ever changing shades of brown and green and grey, we were hurried on the tide, while the surface of the water turned and gyrated like the heads of a rabble in flight as we rushed by the rocks at Bernera ferry. The spokes of the wheel were constantly turned this way and that as the little ship's head was deflected from her course by welling mounds of deep green water. Trickling ribbons appeared on each side where waters collided and flowed together, only to dissolve into swiftly spinning whirlpools that turned and writhed in silent agony.

Soon the broader waters of Loch Alsh opened out before us and once again *Rawanah* sailed over a placid surface that neither bubbled nor twisted beneath her keel. The little terminus of the railway that wound its tortuous way past Strome Ferry and Achnasheen through the heart of the wild Highlands to Inverness lay at the base of the hill to starboard, a plume of white steam marking the end of a train in the station. Soon the ferry slipped past and we were through the Kyles, while before us the sea opened up like a promised land.

But what a lovely stretch of sea ! Of all the places on this Highland coast that should delight the heart of a sailing man, the Firth of Lorne or Loch Fyne notwithstanding, I think this Inner Sound by the Kyle of Loch Alsh, with its wide stretches of open water, its islets dotted about like islands in a model lake—Pabay, Longay, the Crowlin Group, and in the distance Scalpay, Raasay and the ever changing outline of Skye—this, I say, is the most enticing cruising area of any I know.

We would fain have sailed from one island to another, exploring them all, but already the watery looking sun was sinking behind the peaks of the Coolin Hills, and soon we should be left out here in darkness. The skipper pored over the Clyde Cruising Club's *Sailing Directions*, that fascinating and invaluable guide for the whole west coast.

' We'll work up into Broadford Bay,' he said at last. ' They say there's a good anchorage near a landing pier.'

The wind fell and as twilight turned the hills of Skye into a sharp peaked jet black wall against the fading sunset, we stole quietly towards a light on shore and let go in seven fathoms.

H. A. nodded to two white shapes that lay half a cable nearer the shore. No light showed on either of them ; they appeared to be just little motor boats whose owners were probably snugly at home. But my skipper liked them not.

' We'll clear out first thing in the morning, M. G.' he said. ' It's too crowded here.'

And we did. A strong wind blew from over the highlands of ' bonnie isle ' and by nine o'clock our mainsail and staysail were set. On the heather land beyond the shores of the bay an assortment of wooden bungalows had grown up, like mushrooms after a night's rain. One or two had verandahs and pink roofs, and a line of telegraph poles revealed a road.

' My God,' exclaimed H. A. when he saw them. ' We might be in Surrey ! '

By seven o'clock that evening we staggered—I choose the word for its exact description— into Staffin Bay almost at the northernmost tip of Skye. The need for fresh provisions had made us drop our anchor in Portree harbour, the wettest spot, I believe, in the British Isles with its 100 inches of rain a year, where we saw more yachts together than I had seen in any other anchorage north of Tobermory. There were four.

Then on again down the long harbour and out into the Sound of Raasay for another twenty miles further north. A strong westerly wind was blowing and *Rawanah* was roaring along comfortably rigged with small jib, staysail, double reefed mainsail and mizen with three turns rolled in the booms. And when we rounded Garrafad Head and opened up Stenchol Island within the wide expanse of the Bay, black squalls screamed down on us from the Trotternish Hills whose grim heights were smothered in devilish looking storm clouds.

Those clouds did not move. Like black phantoms they played about the heads of the mountains and hurled great gusts of cold, rain laden wind at us, so that we heeled to our lee rail first on one tack and then on the other, while the sheets thundered on the deck and the jib barked like a machine gun as we beat slowly up towards the shore.

Night closed in quickly with an ominous increase in the viciousness of the squalls. The sturdy little ketch turned around her anchor and heeled under their onslaught, and the taut cable gave sudden roars of sound against the bobstay, vibrating the ship like bursting shells.

' What would the Minch be like on a night like this ? '

The skipper looked up from the chart spread out on the cabin table. He wore his hornrims and looked incredibly wise in the lamp light.

' I've read that it's no place for a small boat ', I answered, ' in heavy weather.'

Indeed I wondered just what those seventeen exposed miles of sea between Skye and East Loch Tarbert would be like on a night like this, with their strong tides and patches of rocks. The Minch, I had heard, has a bad name for its broken water.

' The glass is still dropping.'

H. A. turned from the barometer and encouraged the fire with the poker while our wet clothes hung around the stove and slowly steamed. The thought of lying here with none too much shelter, rolling and groaning to the squalls, windbound maybe for two or three days and unable to get ashore in the dinghy was not encouraging. Staffin Bay looked a gloomy, deserted sheet of angry water before night closed in, and our only neighbours appeared to be three or four fishing boats that lay a mile away close to the island.

On the morrow the glass had risen nearly a tenth and there were two patches of blue on the greyness above. But still the wind howled down from the hills and the black clouds were still hiding the peaks in gloom.

' What do you feel about it, M. G. ? '

I nearly dropped the cup I was washing when confronted with the question with so little warning. Through the port hole I could see Staffin Bay, cold, grey and windswept, and the beach a land of rocks and pebbles and patches of coarse grass. It looked like a picture from one of the dead planets where nothing lived and no flowers grew. I put the cup on its shelf and ran the mop around the bowl.

' We've got a tight little ship, skipper, and a self-emptying well ; good charts, and canvas that won't blow away. This place looks like the end of the world. Come on, let's go.'

With the small jib, staysail, double reefed main and mizen, *Rawanah* lurched out into the open. Once clear of Trotternish Point at the end of Skye, she caught the full blast of the westerly wind and heeled to it until her scuppers were gurgling. But no farther would the stubborn little vessel be driven. ' I'll bow so far to you ', she seemed to say, ' and now we'll get going.'

With her decks still clear of any water she shouldered herself over the seas with a steady purposeful lift and scend. It was grand to watch her, and I locked the wheel and let her sail herself to see how well she could look after herself in this big, tumbling sea.

Trodday Island and the Sgeir na Mule slipped away to leeward while we sailed for a time in the smoother water under the shelter of Fladdachuan Island, whose rounded top shone bright green in an unexpected burst of pale sunshine. Then we encountered the bigger swells once more and had the Minch to ourselves. Beyond the horizon the undulating outline of the Hebrides showed every now and then above the wave crests, while away to the north, dim and unreal like fairy isles, the Shiants raised their twin heads.

Slowly the day grew worse and the dark pall in the sky towards the west spread over us, changing the colour of the sea to a more sinister tone while the wind's song in the rigging rose in a shrill harsh cadence. The spray was being blown off the tops of the seas now and stung our faces as we crouched in the well with our sou'westers pulled down to our oilskin collars. Rain came, mingling with the driven spray, a curtain of greyness that cut off the world.

'Can't see a thing,' H. A. shouted in my ear, peering around. A big sea loomed up off the port bow and hovered a moment with its grey-green crest about to tumble over. *Rawanah* luffed up and met the brute with her bowsprit like a brave hound meeting a charging boar. There was a roar of water, a sudden dash of stinging spray, and with a wild leap the little ship dived down into the trough beyond. Then she steadied on her course again, shouldering herself buoyantly over the next sea while the water gushed through the lee scuppers.

'Would you have a look at the chart?' suggested H. A. as he took the wheel. 'Tarbert will be a foul place to make if it's going to be as thick as this.'

Below it was warm and snug, and so far nothing had come adrift. *Rawanah* had been planned to be comfortable and orderly even at sea—with deep shelves and permanent lashings and locker doors that opened fore and aft and not athwartships—and, thanks to her naturally tidy skipper, as a rule nothing does get adrift during bad weather. So many yachts are both badly planned and badly skippered—untidiness being a sin aboard a small boat—that one half expects to find the cabin in a state of oil soaked chaos when at sea.

I didn't like the look of East Loch Tarbert on the chart with visibility as low as it was today. There appeared to be too many unmarked rocks 'awash at LWOS' right in the fairway with nothing but leading marks far up the loch to guide one. In an hour we should be closing in with the comparatively low lying land, and it was essential to hit off the entrance correctly with this sea running. From the chart I decided that the wide entrance south of Scalpa Island would be easier to make. The northern entrance, the other side of the island, looked mighty narrow and difficult for strangers to pick up in thick weather.

Rawanah gave a wild lurch as I climbed the companion and left me hanging in mid air for a moment. Then I stood in the hatchway with my elbows on the slides, while the wind roared under my sou'wester and the rain lashed my cheek. H. A. was sitting with one hand on the upper spokes of the wheel and his head inclined to the blast, while the rain coursed down his glistening oilskins and joined the water gurgling in the corner of the well. I liked him because he never once suggested running back to Staffin or Portree.

'Can't see a thing,' he called out. His voice sounded weak and echoless as it fled on the wind. 'Did you make anything of the chart?'

I nodded and instantly regretted it. A thin, icy trickle began its tedious journey down the back of my neck and did not warm up till it had reached the middle of my back.

Rawanah seemed to pause a moment, rose up with her head high in the air, hovered and fell forward with a fine scending movement. A bucket of spray scattered into the mainsail and the back of a big grey sea, flecked with white, rose up beyond the skipper's head and was lost in the murk astern. I turned and screwed up my eyes to look to windward, and the roar in my ears became almost deafening until I took off the sou'wester.

The seas were splendid in their anger and only needed some sunshine to show up the lovely translucent green of their crests. Now they were grey with a tinge of deep bottle green far down between the lacework patterns of foam. It was the unfathomable shade of the Atlantic itself and we felt, as our little ship breasted the seas and hurled herself over them, that we were sailing now beyond the ken of man, on the fringe of the unknown ocean. The Minch was showing us a fine big sea, but not quite the vicious, dangerous, overwhelming turmoil we had expected from the stories. Maybe all that happened away north there over the dreaded Shiant banks.

'This is better than that godawful Thames Estuary of yours,' remarked the skipper as he sucked a drowned pipe. 'These seas aren't like muddy cliffs.'

Poor skipper once had a bad dusting in the Swin and his respect—badly expressed as it was —for the sandy waters of Essex and Kent in bad weather is deep seated.

An hour later the grey rocks of Scalpa Island were looming through the rain off to starboard, the base of the cliffs a cauldron of flashing white. *Rawanah* was put before the wind for a minute while the jib halyards were swigged up and the storm jib rolled up—a far better way than trying to deal with a flogging sail and flaying sheets while the ship plunges wildly head to wind—and the mizen was hurriedly run down and stowed. Under double reefed main and staysail she still rushed towards the wide loch and its hidden rocks faster than we liked.

'Do you know where the rocks are, M. G.?'

'M' yes. We keep a line open of the highest point of Scotasay Island and—er—Sgeir Griadach.'

'Can you see the island?'

'No, I'm damned if I can.'

'Or the rock?'

'No.'

Rawanah rushed on. The sea was easier in here under the lee of Ghreosabhaigh Head, but there was still a lumpy swell, and as it was almost low water I reckoned we should be able to detect any rocks dangerously near the surface.

'Blast this rain. Can you see anything now, M. G.?'

'No. Keep her as she's going. Perhaps half a point more north.'

Rawanah rushed on.

'There you are, skipper.' A triumphant note in my voice now. 'That's one of them, under the staysail there. Just awash.'

Every now and then, as a swell burst into white and subsided, a grim black mound, like a basking shark, appeared on the grey water to leeward.

H. A. looked at the rock with a wry smile.

'How many more like that?'

'Oh dozens,' I lied airily, for I had just glimpsed our next mark, 'only they're a bit more submerged than that one—a foot or two.'

The skipper gave me an old fashioned look.

'Well, take the wheel, M. G., while I shut myself up in the cabin with my fingers in my ears and wait for the bump.'

But we circumnavigated all the rocks, reefs and submerged dangers without concussion and came to rest—or rather, let go—off the little quay at East Loch Tarbert. While we stowed the sodden canvas and the water poured up our sleeves we looked at the grey, rocky, wind-swept, treeless, rain soaked land with its deserted hillside and grey slated deserted looking houses, looked at one another and laughed. A hollow, humourless, callous sound.

' Well, we've come a long way to get here', was H. A.'s comment as we went below and draped our sodden clothes around the stove, ' and here we are.'

We did not go ashore that day. There was nothing to go ashore for, and our wet clothes already filled half the cabin, while I was enjoying a nasty twinge of rheumatism all down one leg from too much damp.

That night a gale blustered up the West Loch, funnelled through the narrow valley separating the two loch heads, and tore at our rigging in bursts of fury. *Rawanah* heeled first one way and then the other as she swung around on her anchor, and her cable drew itself savagely across the bobstay with familiar deafening roars.

All next day it rained and it blew and we had the coal stove burning for warmth. I went ashore for exercise and stores and got little of either, for the rain came down in torrents, the wind nearly blew me off my feet, and every step brought a sharp pain down one side. A few inhabitants had appeared and some excitement was obviously afoot at the base of the hill over-looking the village. A dozen or so men were grouped together, hands deep in overcoat pockets, shoulders bent and hats turned well down, with half a dozen soaked and dejected looking ani-mals that might have been cows. I have never seen such angular, wet looking cows. A sandy haired youth, his hands also buried in his coat pockets, enlightened me.

' Aye, yonder's the cattle fair.'

I asked him, after a difficult pause, while the information and the rain soaked in, what time of the year they could count on fine weather.

' The weather's a' richt. It doesna rain quite so haird as a rule—aye, but it usually blaws.'

There was no congenial local inn with a warm, matured smoky bar, and friendly local inhabitants to talk to about the weather, the sea, boats, fishing and men's topics. There was no mail for us, no papers, no new books to be found on shore. The last tourist had fled and the ' Olde Tea Shoppe ' sign boards swung creakily in the wind with no tea behind the cold, empty windows.

I went back to *Rawanah*, changed once more and waited for the next excitement of the day —the thrice weekly arrival of the inter-islands motor vessel, *Loch Ness*.

At three that afternoon the radio mocked us with a precious voice from Wimbledon which minced : ' It is really *too hot* for the players this afternoon.' And the weather report spoke of a heat wave in Glasgow and record high temperatures in England. The sound of the wind in the rigging and the rain beating on deck almost drowned the wireless as we stoked up the coal fire !

The second morning here a pale sun tried to shine through the hurrying clouds, looking at first like a glistening ball of white wool ; but the wind still shrieked at us through the gully between the lochs, and we could even feel the spray driven off the head of West Loch over the narrow neck of land into the East Loch where we lay. Time was getting on ; I should soon have to return to the office desk with its accumulated correspondence and routine work, and H. A. was thinking of his long passage through the Irish Channel home to Salcombe. Exploring the rock-strewn Hebrides in weather like this was out of the question.

'What about it, M. G.? It's a fair wind to Skye.'

'O.K. with me, skipper. Anything to get out of this barren hole.'

With something of eager anticipation in our veins we set the mainsail with three reefs and the storm jib halfway along the bowsprit, and double lashed the pram and all the loose deck gear. And we kept the fire burning, for the N.W. wind was still cold and moist as it burst in from the wild Atlantic.

Rawanah hurried out through the narrow passage north of Scalpa Island. The gulls flew up from their rocky perches, wheeling and crying plaintively. And *Rawanah* began to curtsy to the swell. We were homeward bound.

As we left the Hebrides astern the sun came out again, pale, but welcome, and the Minch turned a vivid green, flecked here and there with white. To the north the Shiants stood out like the peaks of subterranean mountains against the horizon, and the Sgeir-inoe lightvessel pitched at her mooring three miles off the port bow. Over the bowsprit end the familiar outline of Skye already showed, like great rocks on edge, over the wave tops. There was something urgent, excited, in the ship's tempo as she burst her way through the tumbling water, rolling and hurrying on her course, and the good wind blew up from astern, pulling at her reefed sails and snoring through the shrouds. There was a feeling of relief to be at sea again, away from that barren, rocky hole that we should ever think of as a grey place of cold and wind and wet. I began to long for the sight of trees and green grass and heather once more, and more so for the chance to meet congenial, friendly people whose faces did not bear the glum imprint of damp chill winds and mists and a grim, treeless rocky landscape.

'Just look at the Hebrides now,' I said, facing the wind. Over their rounded heads a pall of black cloud still lay, draped like a shroud, while the rest of Scotland that we could see shimmered under bright sunshine. 'Because they're the first land the Atlantic meets do you think it eternally vents its wrath on the islands?' The poetic thought moved me.

But H. A. was thinking of other things.

'Biscuits or more cake, M. G.?'

I gave in and accepted both.

The deep green seas rushed up astern with angry heads bent on pooping us; but as soon as our smooth wake touched them, they appeared to change their minds and subside into quiet swells, like a blustering bully who suddenly meets his equal and adopts a mild demeanour. It was fascinating to watch how the 'slick' left by a fine run aft seemed to prevent the seas from breaking, almost as though we were dropping spots of oil or towing a long warp. I have met critics who tell me I make some of my boats too fine in the quarters, 'they lack power, you know, and all that'; but in sailing a boat in *really* bad conditions and having to run before a really vicious sea, I stick to my guns and insist on as fine a run aft as the vessel will stand. If the easy quarters lack power, a properly designed midship section should make up for any loss. More than once I have been thankful for a fine run, for I have sailed in boats which have had fat quarters, and when running before a nasty sea the disturbed wake would encourage the seas to break. The ships of olden days, the snell wave-floaters of our Norse forebears, were not given wonderfully fine runs from amidships aft to no purpose, even though they may not have been metacentroids.

166

Once under the lee of Trotternish again with the wind now on our starboard quarter we hove-to and set the single reefed mizen and the staysail. Then in the smooth water past Altavaig Island and Staffin Bay, past the steep rocky cliffs of Skye to starboard and the distant peaks of South Rona to port, *Rawanah* flew with her lee scuppers agurgle. From the cold heights of the land, where even now on this sunny day heavy clouds gathered about the mountain peaks, came whistling squalls, and for sheer joy as I sat astride the wheel gripping the tugging spokes with the roar of the bow-wave and the hiss of our wake in my ears I sang aloud:

> Speed bonnie boat, like a bird on the wing,
> Over the sea to Skye.

After those two days lying weather bound, wind blown and rain soaked, it was a delight to be sailing again, rushing along with a strong fair wind, parting the waters of Raasay Sound into torrents of creamy white, quivering with the exhilaration of our going. It was good to be able to see pine woods again, trees and shrubs and the beautiful purple heather growing on the hills as the land slipped past ; it was fine to catch a glimpse of two little white yachts lying far up Portree Harbour as we rushed by. And the gulls had come back with their wheeling cries and those absurd clowns, the puffins, were scattering from our path once more, with little heavy bodies, such fast-flapping wings, and such a poor performance! As they struggled to rise clear of the surface and their fat little tummies bashed the wave tops again and again, one wanted to throw them up with a flying start and a ' Gee up, birdie, git goin' ! ' The puffins are the comic relief of a dour country.

Down the passes of Loch Sligachan and Loch Ainort came violent squalls with black clouds that blew their furies at us and then hung back, as though contented with their work, to hover around the peaks once more. Through the narrows between Scalpay and Strollamae we drifted in the late afternoon almost becalmed, while the sky faded to grey and a drizzle began to fall. Then once clear of the high land and heading out into the Inner Sound with Pabay off our bowsprit and the low shores of Broadford Bay on our starboard beam, we had the wind once more, but a tired wind now, showing signs of distress with the setting sun.

' Shall we make Loch Alsh before sundown, do you think ? '

The skipper's question had been bothering me, for these are not pleasant parts to be left in after dark with the possibility of a blow from the west during the night. But the good wind held enough to give us perhaps four knots with all reefs shaken out, and steadily we closed in with the lighthouse that stood sentinel to the Kyles. A rusty, round ended little Glasgow puffer with her stump mast at a rakish angle and her thin funnel right aft belching black smoke passed by bound for Portree, a tumble of white at her bluff bows. She was the only vessel we had passed all day.

As darkness softened the outline of the Highlands and drew the shadows together like the folds of a net we stole through the narrows and into the silent entrance of Loch Na Beiste, just behind Kyle Akin.

' M. G., the place is crowded ! '

Like white phantoms in the deeper shadows of the loch two yachts lay at anchor a quarter of a mile from one another : one a small steam yacht, the other looked like a 60 ft. motor yacht.

I was inwardly glad to see company and looked forward perhaps to talking to the motor yacht's owner in the 'morning, but now after a fine sail of close on seventy miles we were both content to fall into our bunks and sleep.

English voices greeted us from the other yacht in the morning as we rowed ashore, a friendly family who asked about *Rawanah* and warned us the way over the hills to Kyle Akin was treacherous and boggy. If we couldn't make it, could they give us anything we needed as they had plenty of provisions ? We thanked them across the water and I suggested hopefully that an exchange of visits might be very interesting and pleasant, for the owner looked a good type and his two daughters had attractive voices. But the skipper said : ' We haven't much time to lose if we want to make Tobermory tonight.'

Suppressing the mutinous feeling that a sociable day idling in Loch na Beiste, discussing Highland cruising with fresh people, and perhaps tramping over heather covered hills beyond the shores of the loch, would be time well spent, I floundered over the two miles of rough crag and bogland into Kyle Akin, bought provisions from a sour faced woman and an utterly charming old Scottish butcher (who alas, spoilt his droll remarks with an account of the Western Brothers' latest joke) and returned to the ship. The engine was already spluttering on to the still water. We at once got under way, smiled and waved politely to the family aboard the motor yacht who wished us a pleasant passage, and turned our stern resolutely (or wistfully) on social philanderings.

All day long there was not so much as a cat's paw of wind. The sun played on the bright greens and browns of the hills, the varying greys of the rocks and the purple patches of heather as the tide hurried us through the narrows of Kyle Rhea once more and shot us out into the wide, mirror-like expanse of the Sound of Sleat. All day the Handybilly *k'chugged* while the skipper periodically attended to the stern bearings, and the little ketch crept past the shores of Skye on the one hand and of Inverness-shire on the other. Scarcely another boat appeared in the shimmering distance other than the purposeful mail boat that rumbled past on her way to Stornoway.

Our little ship began to bow with solemn dignity to the slow Atlantic swell while the great mounds of Rum, Eigg and Muck changed positions imperceptibly as the stars cross the heavens.

The sun neared the dark heads of the Highlands beyond Ardnamurchan and before Ardmore Point was quite open of the white lighthouse, we stopped our engine and floated noiseless, while the skipper waited for the 9.30 weather report. Three weather reports per diem was the skipper's allowance, and we stopped the engine, or hove-to, or raced back to the ship in the dinghy, as the case may be, whenever another B.B.C. report was due. It was as twice before that day : ' Fair settled weather, winds light to indefinite.'

In the dark, almost at midnight, we crept into the anchorage at Tobermory and picked a berth amongst the yachts whose riding lights stretched out long oily fingers across the water towards us.

And next morning we sailed with a light following wind, straight out through our little passage inside Calve Island, and on through the now familiar Sound of Mull, where the calm water sparkled in the bright sunshine and even the Lady Rock and Duart Castle looked less grim than when we had sailed past bound north. In a flat, hot calm, with the aid of the in-

168

valuable Clyde Cruising Club's book, we left the still waters of the Firth of Lorne and picked our way cautiously into a narrow passage by the Toad of Lorn, a place like an Essex creek whose sedge-covered banks have suddenly crystallized into weed-strewn rocks, and let go in but three fathoms. The anchorage of Puilldobhrain is no wider than its name, a gully in fact between Seil Island and mounds of grass-covered rocks, while the little island itself is joined to the rest of Scotland over the narrow Clachan Sound by a single stone bridge which has the distinction of being the only bridge to span part of the Atlantic—or so they say.

Still anxious to make the Clyde ere I had to return to London, we left the 'Puilldoran' nook and pushed on again at 9 o'clock next morning with a fine following wind, passing no fewer than three yachts in Scarba Sound. We gazed into the dreaded pass of Coirebrechain, where at spring tides a fresh wind will turn it into its own name, a 'cauldron of the speckled sea', a place in which, exaggeration has it, no boat may live. Through the tide race of Dorus Mhor and so to Crinan by lunch time : then through this entrancingly pretty canal and its fifteen locks to Ardrishaig in three hours and a half. And then in a fresh south-westerly breeze we were locked out into the harbour and beat down Loch Fyne having a late tea below while the ship sailed herself.

That night we sounded our way into the little bay north of Barmore, a useful anchorage about two miles north of Loch Fyne's East Loch Tarbert. We had anchored here the previous summer in *Awara,* and as on that first occasion when we had approached cautiously right up to the pebbly beach before finding bottom, and listened to the continuous gurgle of a hidden burn, a curious feeling of foreboding had come over me ; so again this time I looked around with almost a sense of apprehension at the still bay with its overhanging rocks and dank sea-weed, the silent phalanxes of the trees and the impenetrable shadows in their depths, at the grim turret of the castle peering over the tops of the pines, and above all at the unfathomable water that lay still and ominous beneath our keel. There were shadowy forms of immense jellyfish far down, like ghostly shapes, moving slowly, and as I coiled the lead line it stung my hands as though it had plunged deep into some submarine hell where even the water itself was rank and poisonous.

The sun was low over the hills and the castle stood now in silhouette above the pointed tips of the trees, and for a moment I could imagine a mediaeval baron living there, waiting for the darkness to come to launch a hundred bowmen against us, I could imagine the thud of poisoned arrows left quivering in our decks and coamings, and the clink of swords and shields. I shall always think of the Barmore anchorage as some sinister pool wherein unspeakable horrors have been enacted beneath the frowning keep of the castle—but in reality it is a pleasant little anchorage in westerly to southerly winds and the castle is, I believe, nothing but a castellated house owned by a charming sportsman with none of the traits of my imagined baron !

Through the Kyles of Bute past the Burnt Isles and the anchorage of Colintraive we sailed next day with a brisk southerly wind and a sparkling sun. We were back in the latitudes of fields and hedgerows and plane trees, and man with his wisdom and excellence was represented by little pink-roofed villas and rows of telegraph poles marking metalled roads. We were back in civilisation.

It was but a step now—a matter of one night anchored in Kames Bay near the cluster of yachts at Port Bannatyne for fresh stores and petrol, and a few hours' run up the Firth of Clyde —to the Gareloch. My work was done ; we had got the ship back to the Clyde where H. A. could set off on his long passage home, while I must hurry south by train.

On a hot morning, then, as I stood on the deck of the little Clyde steamer, with that sinking feeling with which I always return to London and work, I waved to *Rawanah* as she headed around Roseneath Point under power, bound home to Salcombe. When I thought of how we had pushed her along over the 400 miles of our short holiday, and then of the 500-odd miles of probably gale-swept sea that waited for her, I thought ' Restless little ketch, you've got a fine courageous skipper,' and I gave her a special fair wind wave.

And I wondered when I should be able to return once more to this wonderful cruising ground of the West Coast.

Nightfall headed for the Estuary.

A Cruise in the Thames Estuary

THE tide was creeping in. Silently its oily fingers were feeling the tiny holes and crevices in the mud, filling them one after the other as the water surged forward. Above the smooth surface of the water little mounds of mud, higher than the rest, stood up like minute islands in a calm sea. But even as I watched, they grew less and less until, one after another, their peaks disappeared and left an unbroken surface to the tide.

Soon the water was around the dinghy, rippling musically under the planks. Sitting on the cabin top I watched the tide advance to the edge of a great hollow where *Nightfall's* keel had left its mark on an earlier ebb. A pool of water lay in this trough wherein I could see little green crabs stalking and staring. Now as the new tide reached the rim it seemed to hover, and then with a sudden rush it poured over the edge until the level welled up and the crater was gone. Its advance, at once timid and omnipotent, was like that of an army stealthily surrounding a doomed capital.

There is an indescribable peacefulness and inevitability about sitting aboard one's boat just waiting for the tide to come in. The responsibility is entirely outside one's own hands and there is no call for haste or impatience, nothing one can do to hurry it or stop it. Waiting for the tide is a soothing pastime that calms one's ordinary impatience more than anything I know.

But waiting thus for the tide to float one's little ship has not always been so serene, I reflected. That time I told about in *The Magic of the Swatchways* when two of us were stranded on the hard Buxey Sands in a leaky little 3-tonner and half a gale blowing was a trial of patience and apprehension. It is when the wind is howling and the seas are roaring on the sands, like a brigade of charging cavalry, bent on smashing up the helpless little vessel, that the tide takes on a new significance and a new threat in its deep voice.

But on this occasion when I had arrived at Heybridge just as my pleasant little 9-ton cutter was settling her keel into the soft mud, and the ebb was pouring seaward as though escaping from the Plague, I felt no desire to stamp and swear and wish to heaven I kept the confounded boat at some place where there was always water. The tide is one of those very few things that I usually accept philosophically, and I was quite happy to settle aboard and wait. It was not as if *Nightfall* would give me four hours of purgatory at an angle of 45 degrees. With her nice full section and shallow keel she took only a slight list and it was no trouble to walk about in the saloon and to adjust the table until it was level.

She was a clever shoal draught design of H. H. Lidstone's and her plans appeared in *The Yachting Monthly* for April 1933, 31 ft. OA, 27 ft. WL, 9 ft. beam and 3 ft. 6 in. draught, with no centreboard. A sharply cambered cabin top gave 5 ft. 9 in. headroom under the beams and the saloon was one of the largest and roomiest I had met in a boat of her tonnage. The garboards met the keel rabbet at a hard angle all along, giving a keel some 15 in. deep and allowing the hull to have a long clean run, so that the ship had a very clean pair of heels. I was very fond of her and had owned her—my eleventh boat—for four years, a record so far as I was concerned!

I had promised to meet Dick on the hard at West Mersea on the morrow for a week's cruise to the Thames, where he hoped to add some notes on shipping to his sketch book. I might have waited a day and come down with him to join the ship at her moorings, but there are times when I have a longing to be alone ; not for long, for I enjoy good companionship, but just for a whole day or maybe two. Solitude that is not persisted in is like a balm ; it helps one to work out of one's system that accumulated nervous strain and irritability that comes from the daily rush of London. Occasionally, when my writing has kept me busy every night in the week in addition to days at the office when the work seems to keep just one day ahead of one, and I suddenly discover that if I catch that 9.13 in the morning and that 6.42 home every evening for much longer, I shall lose what wits I possess, then I find a quiet week-end spent alone aboard the old boat, doing nothing much but just basking in the tranquil peace of nature and the call of the seabirds, is more soothing than anything else I know. And that is how I felt when I joined *Nightfall* on this occasion, tired, mentally exhausted and irritably conscious of a desire, like Garbo, to be left alone.

The ship was upright now and I began to take the gaskets off the tanned mainsail. The staysail was ready to set, for being ochre and oil dressed like *Nightfall's* other sails it was always left made up on its boom. The jib too was all ready to be unfurled on the Wykeham Martin gear. Even as I stowed the canvas gaskets in the cockpit locker the little cutter began to swing around under the urge of the tide, pausing while the water flowed silently around her stern, then breaking free and turning once more. The dinghy already trailed astern as though wondering what we were waiting for.

'NOT MUCH OF HER UNDER THE WATER'

Nightfall on the hard for a scrub at Pin Mill, Suffolk, reveals her shallow hull and the clean run of her garboards up to her counter. There is no severe curve to any of her sections and 'nothing much to stop her going through the water.'

The lower picture shows how, by a cabin top well cambered at the after end, 5 ft. 9 in. headroom was obtained. *Nightfall* was designed by H. H. Lidstone.

[*Photographs by courtesy of R. A. Nicholson*

A CRUISE IN THE THAMES ESTUARY

A light breeze had sprung up from the south and the red streamer at the masthead was standing straight out over the forestay with its end quivering against the blue sky. How good it felt to grasp the halyards, to exert one's physical strength and to hear the merry crackle of the patent sheaves in the blocks. How can one describe the satisfaction with which one returns to the cockpit, unrolls the jib with a jerk on its sheets and then feels the tremor in the tiller that means the ship has now come to life?

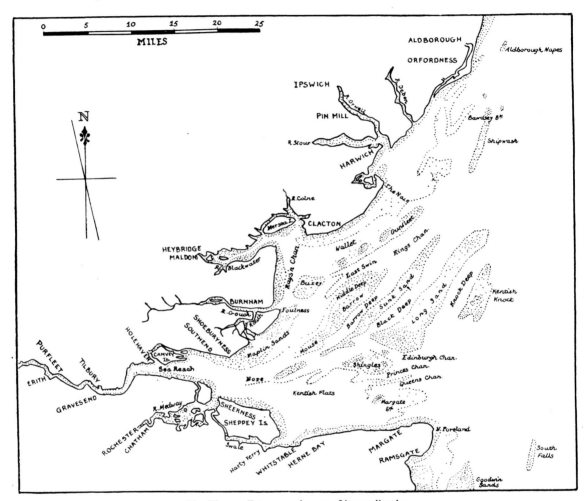

The Thames Estuary and some of its sandbanks.

The Blackwater Sailing Clubhouse dropped astern and slowly, for the flood was running swiftly and the breeze was yet fickle, the tree studded skyline of Osea detached itself from the Millbeach shore and revealed itself as the true island that it is. The breeze hardened and the dinghy's chatter became a continuous surge, and when I lashed the helm and walked forward to set the staysail, *Nightfall* was hurling a fine wave away from her lee bow.

All this was such familiar ground. I had sailed thus, scores of times, dropping down to the

174

first black buoy off Northey Island or carrying on to the anchorage by the pier on Osea, so as to be afloat at low water, yet every occasion had given me the same thrill, the same feeling of satisfaction and of expectancy.

Every mile of the old Blackwater brings to mind some occurrence or other in past sailing days. I recalled with a smile an absurd incident that happened one Friday night twelve years ago in my old fashioned clipper bowed cutter *Puffin II*. I had Tom, an old cruising friend, aboard for the week-end and we were dropping down from the moorings on the ebb, almost smelling our way in the pitch darkness with our little two-stroke motor spluttering under the counter. Unfortunately we stuck on a spit that runs out from the western end of Osea island and the swift running tide soon began to fall away. The mud was fairly soft, however, and as it was a flat calm we stayed on deck quite still trying to get the yacht to settle upright with her keel well in the mud.

When the water had gone she was sitting upright, rather high, it was true, with her bilges well above the mud, but it seemed her keel was firmly holding her and we went below to get supper, feeling very pleased with ourselves. The tea and a brace of steaming hot kippers with toast and butter were on the table when I thought the table was taking a very slight list towards me. Tom's expression would have delighted a strip artist as he exclaimed ' My God, she's going over ! ' and clutched his cup of tea, and the next moment *Puffin* subsided rather than fell right over on her starboard bilge, while the kippers and hot tea and toast and butter descended on to me as I sprawled against the lining ! That was the only time I ever embraced a pair of kippers. I never trusted a sharp bottomed yacht to sit upright without legs after that.

This time I carried on past Osea with the old Barnacle post, a black weedy sentinel, guarding the little bay where two white yachts lay at anchor. Slowly the little cutter forged through the fast running flood until the western end of Mersea Island was in full view over the port bow, with its ever growing spate of houses and the square flint tower of the church peeping above the group of trees in the churchyard on the hill.

For a moment I considered running up into the Quarters for the night, but Bradwell creek looked enticing and I knew that I could easily sail across the river in the morning to pick up my crew.

The flood would soon be done and the greater part of Peewit Island was covered ; indeed, it was now only a stretch of level sedge-covered mud with the heads of the leading beacons barely above the water. The gentle breeze was dying too and *Nightfall* lazily turned up the narrow entrance to the creek to a spot below the first horse, where I let old Cold Nose sink into the bed of the creek with a dull splash.

And soon the tide was slipping smoothly past the grey hull, trickling through the links of the taut anchor cable, hurrying to join the Blackwater ebb that had started running north. The Hour of the Sea, as the French so picturesquely call it, had passed and everything, it seemed, was anxious to join the ebb into the North Sea.

As I made a late tea the sun neared the horizon, a great golden ball that sank quickly behind the Maldon hills, and soon the light became dim in the cabin. I did not light the lamps just yet, but sat instead smoking contentedly and watching the square of the open hatch turn from blue to blue grey, to deeper blue and then imperceptibly to the deep shade of nightfall.

And when I had put the washed-up crocks in their pigeon holes and gone on deck, the dim outline of Peewit Island rose unexpectedly high against the skyline, and the mud banks stood like barriers on either side against the night.

The creek was almost hidden in darkness, but behind a clump of trees beyond the sea wall the moon was hiding, like an actress in the throes of stage fright waiting in the shadow of the wings. As I stood in the hatchway the moon rose clear above the tree tops and her pale fingers began to trace their way across the mud until they reached the edge of the water. Soon her light was advancing, quivering and gyrating in little oily pools of silver, across the smooth-flowing surface.

There was very little ebb left now, a mere trickle, and I drew the dinghy alongside with the idea of exploring the length of the creek at low water. Scarcely a sound broke the stillness as I rowed past the dim forms of the yachts moored in the channel, and the twisted stakes at the quay—the Old Men of Bradwell, I call them—stood grotesquely silhouetted against the starry sky as I drifted past them.

For nearly two miles I rowed between dark banks that glistened where the moontrack lay across them. So still was it that one heard the sucking of the mud, the delicate trickle of little pools pouring through Lilliputian gullies into the stream, and the waning moon, now risen high in the sky, lay still and clear, mirrored faultless on the water. In the light of my torch thrusting its dazzling beam down through two feet of water, evil crabs hesitated, nippers outstretched, their baleful black eyes staring, and transparent shrimps hovered uncertainly amid waving fronds of weeds, bright red stars in place of their eyes. There was beneath the keel of the drifting dinghy another world, a world of silence and cold, of flowing darkness and waving fronds, of little red stars that shone in pairs and dashed swiftly hither and thither, a world of which one knew nothing.

From over the fields a dog began to bark, and as though they resented my intrusion so far from the last of the anchored boats, the duck began to call and a peewit gave its shrill cry of warning. There was a clutter of wings, invisible in the darkness, and the cries of the wildfowl went far up the river, becoming faint in the night.

It is curious how such little incidents remain so clearly in one's memory when the more hair-raising episodes of cruising become dim as something distasteful and half forgotten. This power of the human mind to draw a veil over unpleasant memories but to retain with vivid clearness the memory of one's happier moments is a merciful dispensation and leads one to think that, after all, we are intended to enjoy our stay on this earth—even our memory of it—to rise free from the evil of the horrors that men can cause each other. Our memories may not register a true picture of our experiences but who among us is so wise that he can bear to know the whole truth about everything ?

With such thoughts I rowed quietly back to the little ship and found her cabin cosy from the warmth of the lamps.

Dick was waiting on the causeway at West Mersea when I rowed up in the dinghy next morning. He stood with his kit bag leaning against his legs and an incredulous smile on his cheerful face watching another dinghy unload two men and two girls. They were all making a great deal of noise in voices of an East London variety, and one of the girls, a large, fat blonde who seemed to bulge out of her shorts and expand her jumper to its limits, swaggered up the hard swinging her transom.

'I often think', Dick remarked quietly when we were out of earshot, 'that yachting has much to answer for when it attracts caricatures like that one.'

I said that the water as a means of recreation was good for anyone and free to all, but I could not help wondering why so many 'heavy weight' women whose bulbous forms show to such repelling disadvantage in shorts and tight jumpers, or in trousers and sweaters, insist on wearing male attire at all. Sailing and living aboard boats does appear to bring out the bravado, the desire to appear conspicuous, that is latent in so many women, and not so latent in others, and I really believe one sees more flamboyant caricatures, as Dick aptly called them, aboard boats than in any other sport. Maybe the neuter sex, which appears to be gaining ground amongst their boy friends, derives a vicarious joy from these bouncing he-girls in shorts.

There was a light breeze from the north-west with that bright blue sky studded with creamy clouds that always seems to give birth to a north-westerly wind in these islands. Beyond the Quarters where *Nightfall* lay to the flood, beyond the drunken old Nass beacon, the Mersea smacks were beating home in a cluster, like a fleet going into action. Their picturesque sails, brown, grey and incredibly baggy, with here and there a strip of dazzling white where a new cloth had repaired a rent, were converging and cross tacking against the clear horizon, and I thought thus the dreaded marauders, the Norsemen in their 'snell wavefloaters' had made their approach when the Saxons were in the land and the Normans were yet a myth. Many a bloody forage, many a clash of Viking arms against yokel sticks and stones took place in these parts, and the ancient town of Maldon itself once had to send soldiers down the river to harry the Norsemen when their ships grounded by Northey isle.

'Getting under way, Maurice ? '

Dick's face appeared like a friendly moon through the neck of his jersey as he struggled into it, and I helped him stow his shore clothes in the fo'c'sle.

'You bet, me lad. Fair wind for the Crouch and the flood's not done yet,' I told him.

Soon *Nightfall* was picking her way through the smacks, avoiding their long bowsprits as an elderly dame dodges the traffic, and before Dick had quite finished the loaf of bread for lunch we were abreast the solitary chapel that stands on the wall by Sales Point. St. Peter's-on-the-Wall they call it, a quaint flint and brick structure that Cedd the Saxon built in the ninth century for Christian worship. He chose this conspicuous spot from which to dispense the Word of God, for the materials lay readily to hand. An old Roman fort of six centuries before, Othona it was called, lay in ruins under the grass, and Cedd the Saxon found the rich red bricks to his liking. Once a year they hold a service in the chapel, this relic of Othona, lest it should cease to be consecrated ; but at all other times it is just an old barn with a mud floor, a landmark for mariners, and a reminder of those few centuries when Britain was well looked after by the Romans and there were good straight roads throughout the land.

'Gosh ! Only a fathom, Maurice. Is that O.K.? '

Dick let the lead swing back and forth expectantly.

'Ample,' I assured him. 'We're cutting in over the Bachelor Spit and the tide's well up. Take another cast in a minute or two.'

Nightfall hurried on while I pegged the helm and sat on the forehatch. The water was quite smooth and we had brought the wind almost abeam. The sound of the bow wave turning over was music to the ear and I felt then that I would not willingly change places with anyone in the world.

I heard the ' plump ' of the lead followed by a distinct muffled thud as it hit the hard sand over which we were gliding, and grinned at my companion's apprehensive tone : ' Say, there's not more'n five feet here ! '

Dick had no boat of his own at that time, but he had sailed a good deal with other people, and had grown used to 6 ft. draught and the harbours of the South Coast.

When we could distinctly see the bottom passing by with little groups of white shells like constellations of stars in the water, he coiled up the lead line and sat on the cabin top with a wry smile.

' Isn't the channel way over there to leeward,' he asked at last, ' where that white cutter is ?'

We were still moving, although the bottom was quite clear now and the water all around had a strange sandy look.

' So it is, but we're just scraping across the Spit nicely, and who on earth wants to go a mile to leeward only to work up to windward again ? ' I glanced at our wake. ' It's getting deeper already.'

Soon the Buxey beacon, the crossroads signpost, had slipped past half a mile to port and we were in the Rays'n, that shoaling swatchway that leads round the Dengie shore and the Ray sand into the mouth of the Crouch. It was all very familiar to me, this stretch of muddy water with the view of Clacton to the north, the entrance to the Colne, Brightlingsea church, the Blackwater that we had just left, and the level skyline of Foulness Island at the mouth of the Crouch, and I thought how uninteresting it was when one visioned the grandeur, the colouring and the variety of the Scottish west coast. Yet I knew every inch—or thought I did—and somehow when one enjoys sailing and the intricate and cautious navigation necessary in shoal-infested waters, the scenery does not seem to matter a tinker's dam. I remember how I enjoyed later sailing out of Lisbon in a friend's 9-tonner, how familiar it all seemed to be feeling for deeps and swatchways between the extensive sandbanks with a lead line : how accustomed I was to working out swift tides whose waters ran yellow with mud ; and what fun it was when sailing amongst those Tagus banks in another local boat so ideally suited for the purpose, a 24 ft. American catboat.

' What time do we have tea ? ' Dick spoke with some difficulty and I stared at two immense bulges that stretched his cheeks so that he looked like a Cheshire cat.

' Why, drat it, we've only just eaten lunch. What on earth have you got there ? '

He appeared to try to shift the obstructions, but failed.

' Humbugs. Have one ? '

I thoughtlessly passed to leeward of him and reeled faintly against the lee coaming. " Olde English mint humbugs ' have a horsepower rating all of their own. But I managed to stow one of the monstrous, sticky striped things in one cheek, and a gull, hovering to leeward of us, fell into the water and lay with its beak tucked under its wing.

The tide was on the turn as we lay close-hauled up the Crouch, and the forest of masts at

Burnham stood with the hulls beneath them all lying with their sterns towards us. The breeze was dying too, and when we turned into the Roach river we seemed to creep more and more slowly past the sedge-covered banks.

An hour went by and at Dick's pathetic requests I went below and cut doorsteps of bread and jam while the kettle simmered on the stove. My crew was delightfully simple in his tastes ; he never demanded exotic food nor excessive delicacies, and was perfectly content once one grasped the enormity of his capacity, or, as explained in another chapter, his 'tunnage'. Having meals with Dick gave me the impression of toying with food while he settled down to eat.

Nightfall was still making over the strong ebb and from the galley port I could see the Paglesham anchorage and several masts beyond the Potton Island point. But we were not bound for Paglesham, in spite of the attraction of a convivial evening in the 'Plough and Sail'. We were anxious to get into the Thames as soon as possible, for Dick had some sketching to do for a story about London's river in a boys' magazine and I was keen to get into waters I had not visited for a year or two. Thus we turned our bowsprit up the narrow, twisty little creek between Foulness and Potton islands, and as the wind came fitfully across the meadows laden with the scent of green grass and wild flowers, we trickled slowly through the Narrow Gut.

The span on the lift bridge slowly rose at our approach and as we glided under its great black beak and heard the echo of our wash against the piles, Jim the bridgeman leant against the parapet and called down to us.

'You're too late to get out now, sir. The tide's gone.'

We waved acknowledgment, for we knew as well as he that there was no water now on the bar, and that the smooth face of the Maplins would be uncovering for miles off shore, right out to the measured mile beacons beyond which the great ships sailed.

Our anchor cable rattled out and the sails were furled. With a rhythmic clanking, the bridge slowly returned to join the gap across the creek. While I put the gaskets on the mainsail I looked around at the familiar scene. It was very peaceful. Over the saltings a heron rose against the sunset, a black shape with solemn movements, as a pterodactyl might have risen over a prehistoric land. The sky was darkening and in the east night was already creeping upon us stealthily. But the tinge of orange that had glinted in the rays of the setting sun promised us a breeze on the morrow.

By the time supper was over *Nightfall* had taken the ground, but with the aid of the boathook we had felt out a soft patch and she settled at only a slight list to starboard.

'She generally seems to settle to starboard,' Dick remarked unsuspectingly.

'Yes,' I told him. 'The skipper's berth is that side.'

A well trained yacht should never let her owner down.

High water, when there would be four to five feet over the bar, was at 3 a.m. In spite of his keenness to get into the Thames, Dick groaned aloud when I set the alarum for half-past one a.m.

'My God, Maurice, I always thought such hours were a pure myth.'

The creek was very still when we turned out in the darkness. The moon was high in the sky

179

and the stars were brilliant, a soft breeze, as slight as a maiden aunt's caress, with the same hint of chilliness about it, was blowing across the marshes, and I was reminded of the *Merchant of Venice* :

> In such a night as this, when the sweet wind
> Did gently kiss the trees . . .

Nightfall was afloat. When her mainsail and jib were set a stronger puff sent her masthead reeling darkly against the sky as she headed towards the bar. From the foredeck as I coiled the halyard falls I could see Dick's generous form at the tiller and the outline of the banks as they slipped away on each side.

Soon our little ship began to curtsy with the slightest of movement. We were nearly over the bar now.

I put the boathook overboard and felt the hard sand. At that instant the ship tremored, paused, rose on a slight swell and seemed to glide on in the darkness.

' Touched that time, skipper.'

I felt the depth again. The boathook still seemed only to jab the water before it encountered the hard bottom. But we were still moving.

' Look, there's a beacon or something.'

Dick pointed at an angular shape that slipped past to leeward.

' I think we should have gone the other side of that,' I remarked. ' But it doesn't matter now. The water's getting deeper. We're across now.'

As I said it we both half fell forward suddenly and the dinghy sidled up and banged the stern.

I could see the whites of Dick's teeth in the darkness.

' What we really need ', he remarked with a chuckle, ' is someone who can navigate.'

I jumped into the dinghy, cast off and sculled around the ship, sounding every now and then with the oar. As I thought, the channel—now about five feet deep in the middle—was just under our lee bow. The tide was still rising and with the deeper water to leeward we should soon sail off.

Nightfall looked ghostly lying there in the darkness with her sails drawing, for we had put out the cabin lamps to enable us to see.

' She's off, Maurice.'

Almost before I had made the painter fast again the little cutter was sidling through the water, and for the next three quarters of an hour we sailed over the Maplins with a steady three feet of water under our keel.

The white occulting light of the South Shoebury buoy on the edge of the sands glared at us across the water. Slowly we discovered that it was drawing abeam instead of passing astern. The fierce London ebb had set in, and with this light breeze that would probably die before dawn we should merely drift miles astern.

For the second time that night *Nightfall's* anchor dropped with a rattle of chain, and with her dark wings folded she lay on the edge of the Maplins waiting for the tide, periodically lit up by the light from the gas buoy. And far away in the middle of the estuary red and green and white lights steadily moved as the shipping of London River passed us by.

A CRUISE IN THE THAMES ESTUARY

It was broad day when we awoke again and the tide was almost done. Away over on the other side, hull down, two barges crept along the Sheppey shore with only their brown sails above the horizon. A Norwegian steamer, her decks stacked high with timber, was forging up river with a white bone at her bluff bow.

With a snoring breeze from the north-west we were away heading up river past the Nore and the end of Southend pier and the tall beacons on the Isle of Grain. With the strong morning flood under us we soon had the Chapman Pile lighthouse abeam with the Blyth Sands covering on the south side of the river, and far ahead at the end of Sea Reach we could make out the Mucking light.

What history is bound up in these places on London's waterway, what romance must have been enacted at all the ancient landing places. Every bend in the river, every name calls to mind some episode in history, from the very Pool of London itself, down past Limehouse Steps where many a small company has put to sea in an ill-found ship, past Deptford where Samuel Pepys saw the first English-built yacht launched nearly three centuries ago, Greenwich and Woolwich, inseparable from our naval history, and on past Purfleet where the Virgin Queen inspected her fleet before it met the Spanish Armada and is said to have given name to the place with the exclamation : ' Oh, my poor fleet ! ' Personally I don't believe this story, because if Purfleet wasn't named until Elizabeth suggested it, how could the Queen make a date with her fleet at an unnamed rendezvous ?

But we cannot quibble over the truth of history for we are passing the gaunt iron beacon on the other side of the sea wall, so like a woman standing with feet apart and arms akimbo that it is well named the Lady of Canvey, and the Chapman pile light on the mud flats is already a mile or more astern. Ahead of us around the next bend in the river drifts the smudge of Tilbury where the funnels of the great liners stand smoking, and far beyond, in the dim distance the pall of London hovers above the horizon like a vast cloud.

Over to port, a little astern of us now, a different kind of smoke cloud is drifting with the wind, a pall of light grey that becomes yellow as it rises against the blue sky. The cement works up the Medway are pouring out their contribution towards the smoke screen that marks the Kentish shore. And down wind a sickening smell of oil assails our nostrils from the great tanks at Shellhaven.

' That's one of the Coastal Lines boats,' Dick remarked, ' that black chap with the zig-zag on the funnel. There's a rather fine tanker coming down astern of her. I'll make a note of her.'

While I jilled *Nightfall* around just out of the steamer channel, Dick hauled out his sketching materials and rapidly made the most pleasing little drawing of the tanker, long, lean and black with a snow white smear at her frowning bows.

And thus two days were spent while we chased steamers and barges, mud hoppers and tramps, and had our fill of the daily pageant of shipping that passes up and down the most historic waterway in the world.

The second day brought a very fresh and squally S.W. wind with leaden clouds and rain, and in the general murk we plunged and leapt over the white crests in the middle of Sea Reach, with four rolls in our mainboom and only the staysail set. Twice we left *Nightfall* hove-to while Dick sketched an approaching steamer, and I sat wedged on the floor of the cockpit.

'I want to get the shape of the bow wave better,' he explained. 'Look how she's throwing it away off her weather bow. You've got to get that right for illustrating.'

A number of marine artists could do with some more careful study of ships in action, and a small boat is a fine place for making notes.

The next day found us at anchor in the narrow ditch by Holehaven.

'I've got all the notes I want for the time being,' said Dick when we went on deck and sniffed the fresh morning air. 'So where shall we go?'

The glass had fallen a little and the clouds were flying low over the Kentish hills with a fresh wind from the S.W. It might blow hard and I had no wish to taste the long passage down Swin with the cruel sands baring their teeth on either side in thick weather.

'We'll hunt the weather shore', I told him, 'and slip along the Kent side.'

'O.K., Chief. C'mon, let's go!' he cried unnautically in the best film voice, and as soon as breakfast was cleared away *Nightfall* began to curtsy in the rough and tumble outside. With three rolls in her mainsail and the staysail only set she seemed to elbow her way across the seas with a fine flurry off her weather bow. In oilskins and sou'wester I sat against the lee coaming in the cockpit where I could watch from close to the lee deck our bow wave leaping and frolicking away to leeward, and see the Kentish shore rise up and disappear again and again behind the great crests of the seas. Stretched out comfortably on the athwartship seat with his arm over the tiller, Dick sang happily and nursed the old cutter over the steeper seas that came tumbling towards us with a menacing rush in their crests.

'There'll be a hefty sea here when the flood begins to run,' he called out once, and I nodded as *Nightfall* hovered for an instant and dropped into a deep, grey hollow. A fountain of spume shot away to leeward and the sea rolled away towards the Southend shore, its back traced with a pattern in white.

'D'you mind taking the helm, Skipper,' Dick asked, 'while I fill the old pipe?'

Once up on the sailing seat with my feet braced against the lee coaming I was almost deafened by the roar of the wind under my ear flaps. It was better with the sou'wester off, although the wind was laden with salt spray and every now and then a heavier dollop of water would be shot out to windward, only to be carried back to land on deck. The wind seemed to be hardening appreciably and *Nightfall's* lee deck was being washed by the seas more frequently now. With her full sections it was very rarely that I had ever been able to get her rail under; like all shallow boats, she sailed best at only a slight heel and when the covering board came awash it meant she was being pressed too hard.

For a time I hesitated about rounding-to and putting in a couple more rolls in the mainsail, but we were getting under the partial lee of the Grain Spit and would soon have the wind on our quarter. Also the flood tide would begin to run in about an hour's time and we should need plenty of canvas to drive over that.

The black and white check light buoy on the end of the Jenkin Swatchway slipped past to port, dropping out of sight and rolling drunkenly, with cascades of water pouring off his weed-covered sides as he bobbed up afresh over the grey waste of water. Farther away to leeward a line of white marked the breakers on the Nore Sand and the shoal itself could be seen each time we rose on a crest, like a flat motionless pancake of grey and brown surrounded by tormenting seas.

Quite suddenly, it seemed, the water became subdued as we hurried through the swatchway between the sands and opened up the mouth of the Medway with the stone forts of Sheerness frowning against all comers. The last of the ebb was still pouring out, but it had lost some of the fierceness that had made it unapproachable on more than one occasion on previous cruises.

'Going through the Swale?' Dick asked with his pipe between his teeth.

I shook my head, for it would be no joke in a wind like this to have to jill around in the narrow creek at Kingsferry swing bridge for maybe half an hour while the bridgekeeper finished a thriller or tried to coax the local train into risking the crossing.

'No, we'll take the outside passage today,' I decided. 'There'll be plenty of lee under Warden cliffs—'

'And a helluva fine beat up to the anchorage at Harty Ferry,' said Dick with a grin.

Along the Sheppey shore, as close as low water would reasonably allow us, *Nightfall* scurried with the strong wind on her starboard quarter. It was joyous sailing, for the young flood had not yet gained its full strength, the sea here was comparatively calm, and we had just enough canvas aloft to be driving the ship heartily without straining her spars.

My companion came out of the cabin with both cheeks exaggerating a self-conscious grin.

'My God, you haven't got *more* of those ghastly humbugs?'

He nodded.

'Ha' one,' he managed to say, and extended a bag of bulging stickiness.

'Well—out of self-defence, then.' And he took the helm while I became horribly involved with the minty horrors.

As the red cliffs near Warden Point came abeam with the green hills of the island rising above them in pleasant undulating curves, the coastline beyond Herne Bay opened out slowly and Whitstable unfolded its rows of stone houses from behind the land. Two of the local ketches with reefed mainsails and spitfire jibs set on their long bowsprits were standing in towards the Street, their black hulls disappearing and rising into view against a smother of spray. Away over to port the Spile beacon could just be seen, a black stake with a topmark in a waste of green water, while beyond it, several miles away, a tramp steamer was making up towards the Thames with the sea flashing white before her bows as she shovelled into it.

'Shouldn't like to be out there,' remarked Dick as we watched her. 'There'd be a helluva sea in the Swin now.'

He was right. The Swin, with the flood running up against the breeze, would be a mass of tumbling breakers, short, steep and vicious, and whether you were battering into them on a long beat from the end of the Whitaker Spit, or running before them with a warp out astern, you would have a bad time for a number of hours with no anchorage for shelter near at hand. I have made that thirty-mile passage from out of the Burnham river down and round the Whitaker and up Swin to the Medway many times in breezy weather, and have always been glad when a boat with less than 4 ft. draught has enabled me to take the short cut through Havengore.

Dick handed me the binoculars and took the helm while I scanned the sea close in to the end of Sheppey. Somewhere between the Mussel Bank off Shellness Point and the Columbine Spit there was a narrow swatchway, the Ham Gat, with three quarters of a fathom in it at

L.W.O.S. With the flood more than two hours old there would be not less than 8 or 9 feet now, and it would save an extra two miles round the end of the Columbine.

Edging up as close as we dare, we were bringing the wind abeam. A sudden squall of wind and rain drove down from the Leysdown hills and blotted out everything. I swore, put the glasses back in the cabin, and picked up the lead line. The Mussel Bank stands out a long way from the shore and we should have to cross over its tip to make the end of the swatchway. For emergencies such as this I always keep my lead with its line made fast on deck, close to the helmsman. A lead line that is kept stored away in a locker and can only be brought out in a tangled mess after a lot of manœuvring amongst other junk, is generally too late to be of use.

' One fathom.'

' Fathom.'

' Five feet. Bear away a bit, Dick.'

Nightfall was roaring along now and the boom was lifting high above the foaming wake as the squalls pressed her forward. The rain was stinging our faces and an exasperating trickle was beginning to explore my back with an icy finger.

' Fathom.'

' And a half—one. Keep her so, south and a bit east.'

We ought to have had another reef in now that we are coming up close-hauled. The squalls are still vicious and one can't see a thing through this rain. Whatever happens we must not get on to the Columbine Sand that's about half a mile under our lee.

' Fathom and a quarter.'

The next sounding was the same. Under the lee of the Mussel Bank at any rate we had fairly smooth water.

' Fathom.'

' Five feet. Bear away, Dick.'

A dull thud shook the yacht and her weather quarter wave curled over and drenched us. The tiller was swinging, lifeless. For one red hot moment I imagined we might have got on the Columbine, but the seas were not big enough to be on a lee shore.

' Ease off the mainsheet, Dick. I'll back the staysail.'

Even as I did so *Nightfall's* head slewed around, hesitated, rose on a swell, and the tiller suddenly came to life again.

' Isn't that the buoy ? '

Dick was pointing through the lee rigging, and sure enough there was the elusive little red buoy, bobbing merrily as we rushed down towards it. We both breathed more freely, and at that instant the rain drove away and revealed Shellness Point, Whitstable Bay and the entrance to the East Swale.

The wind had eased a little, although it was still fresh, and with hardened sheets *Nightfall* threshed close-hauled past the white coastguard cottages and the beacon on the eastern tip of Sheppey. Down to leeward the Estuary was still blotted out in gloom by the rain clouds, but to windward the sky was lightening and a shaft of pale sunlight was piercing the clouds and tipping the hills beyond Faversham with silver.

Like a dog turning round in his basket before settling down, we encircled the anchorage close under the south side at Harty Ferry, sounding until we got two fathoms. Then our hook was let go and the wet canvas stowed.

' Now for the best tea on record,' cried my companion as he disappeared below.

Because it was mid-week we had the anchorage to ourselves. While I pottered about the deck stowing the loose ends of sheets and halyards, the sun spread his warmth down the creek and over the landscape, lighting up the incredible greens of the fields on Sheppey and tingeing the remote hills beyond with the dim purplish-blue that is part of the wonders of Kent. Nowhere else, except in Scotland, can I remember remarking so clearly the blue tint on the trees and fields that is lent by distance as on the Kentish hills. One of the pleasures of cruising along this part of the coast is the different views that open up at every point, each with its own particular shade of colouring. Sea Reach has its view of London's pall, its nearer vision of the smoke cloud of Tilbury, Dagenham and Gravesend. The Medway is speckled with its patches of dun-coloured cement works with purple hills on the horizon. The anchorage in the East Swale is surrounded, at a distance it is true, with green fields of varying shades, and golden corn lands at the right time of the year, while farther along the coast, past Whitstable, Herne Bay and the twin towers of Reculver, where the ancient river Wensum allowed the Roman galleys to pass inside the Isle of Thanet into the Stour and so to Sandwich and Pegwell Bay by an inland route that is no longer there, the land is a different colour, rocky cliffs begin to appear, and . . .

' Come on, Maurice, the eggs are getting cold,' Dick's voice broke in from below. ' I've begun tea.'

The following morning was warm and peaceful with a light southerly breeze and under the mainsail and jib we sailed up to the mouth of Conyer Creek. A long row up the creek in the dinghy, a long walk into Teynham village for stores, and a pleasant lunch off good bread and cheese and beer at the little inn overlooking the quay, and a lazy row back to the yacht, completed the afternoon. Later we got under way and dropped slowly down past our anchorage at Harty until we had rounded the island and sounded our way close in to Shellness Point. Here we let go while the flood tide welled in and slowly filled all the rivers and creeks and gullies in the Estuary. We planned to take the ebb north, to Pin Mill where I intended leaving *Nightfall*.

The tide never seems so slow or so late as when you are waiting for it to turn. As it was, there was no reason for waiting for the ebb to set in before we left, and a little flood to help us weather the Girdler lightvessel would not be unwelcome, for the breeze seemed to be dying.

At six o'clock we got under way with our sidelights filled and ready in the fo'c'sle and some hot Bovril in a thermos flask stowed ready in one of the lockers. As we passed them one by one the red and black conical buoys off the Columbine spit were lifting and falling sluggishly on the swell with no trace of tide past them. It was the hour of high water.

Almost silently, with but a gentle murmur at our bow and a continuous whisper from the dinghy, and the warm westerly breeze keeping our sails quiet, we slipped onward, while a faint greyness spread over the land astern and twilight fell upon us unnoticed. The shore line became indistinct and one by one lights sprang up from the coast until they all but joined in a chain over by Whitstable and Herne Bay. And ahead of us, in the open waste of the Estuary, the lights of the buoys pierced the gathering gloom as far as the eye could see like multi-coloured stars that flashed and winked at each other.

185

With no tide as yet to allow for I set the course for the East Spaniard buoy, and hoped we should pick up his black and white vertically striped sides before it was too dark to see unlighted things. *Nightfall's* compass was set to one side of a rectangular glass panel in the bulkhead and thus could be seen from either side of the well. Its light was an ordinary candle lamp in gimballs whose mellow light was just strong enough for the helmsman to see the card without leaving any glare to blind him.

Away to starboard we could see the red and green and a single white light of a small steamer, or more likely a motor barge, coming up from the Foreland and making up through the Overland Passage from the Hook Sand to the Cant and the Nore. She was taking the route of those countless ships of old that had sailed up and down this coast, the route of the present day barges and small hoppers and little craft across the shoal waters of the Kentish Flats. The great ships of today, the liners and the big ocean going tramps, keep north of the Girdler and hug the deep waters of the Princes Channel and Black Deep. We should be crossing their track within the hour.

While I sat in the lee side of the cockpit with the cabin bulkhead at my back watching our wake and the dim form of our dinghy ever following us, I fell to thinking of the origins of some of these queer names in the old Estuary. How did they get their names, the Spaniard, the Pudding Pan, the Woolpack, the Spile, the Girdler, the Shivering Sand, the Oaze, the Cant, Clitehole Bank, the Pan Sand, the Knock John, the Barrow, the Edinburgh and a dozen others? Whence came the name for the Nore, whose original lightvessel was, I believe, the first of her kind in the world? What has history to tell us of the naming of the Gilman, the deep that leads past the Red Sand into the Alexandra Channel?

' Isn't that a buoy, through the lee rigging ? '

I turned at the mate's sudden query and peered across the dark water, and sure enough there was an indefinite shape looming out of the murk. It drew abreast, perhaps half a cable's length away, and I put a spot light from the torch on it.

' Black and white vertical stripes and a topmark. That's the East Spaniard all right,' I said. ' Now you can leave the Girdler flash to starboard and edge up a bit to wind'ard of that white flash every 5 seconds. You'll see it again presently. There you are, right over the bowsprit. That's the East Red Sand buoy and we'll keep well to port of him for the ebb's setting us down to the eastward now.'

From the rigid attitude of the mate and his silence I judged he was impressed into speechlessness, but as I went below to have another look at the chart his voice followed me : ' I suppose it's all right, but—I don't think he knows much about it really ! '

In the light of the cabin I recalled another occasion five years previously when in my old Bawley cutter *Storm* another fellow and I had left the East Swale at nightfall and made a similar passage across the Estuary, bound for Heybridge. On that occasion, which formed a chapter in a previous book, the night was warmer to begin with, there was untold phosphorescence in the water, and the heavens were a mass of stars, a night indeed in a hundred. Tonight only a few stars appeared here and there and the waning moon seemed late in rising above the clouds over the eastern horizon. The wind, too, was cooler and we were glad of our sweaters and coats, while below the coal stove gave a pleasant ruddy glow and an atmosphere of cosiness from the chill night air that seemed to embrace one as one entered the cabin.

A CRUISE IN THE THAMES ESTUARY

The powerful white flash of the Girdler lightvessel swept the waters but a mile or two to leeward, lighting up our tanned sails so that they stood out in ruddy curves against the sky for an instant, then passing on to leave us in darkness for another half-minute. Gradually the flashes became less intense and soon the white occulting light of the East Oaze came in line with the rapid flashes of the Barrow as we felt our way across the Oaze Deep. Not far away it seemed on our port bow—although it must have been at least two miles—the baleful red eye of the Mouse lightvessel glared at us every twenty seconds. It was not many years ago that I could remember this light being green and causing some confusion to foreign ships who mistook it for a *wreck* light buoy.

I looked around and tried to count the different lights that I could see winking, occulting, group flashing and fixed in red, green and white, but every time fresh ones appeared as they or we rose on a swell. This Estuary is a maze of lights, and some of them are changed occasionally just to liven the interests of the hapless mariner who tries to cross the puzzle of sand banks and shoals with a ten-year-old chart. Although I enjoy the intricacies of navigation in the Thames Estuary under fair conditions, the very size of its area and the complexity of its channels and dangers make it a terrible cauldron of trouble for small ships that are caught out here in heavy or very thick weather.

'The wind's dropping, I think,' remarked Dick. He had lit his pipe after a solid meal in the cabin, and now as he sat at the helm, a dim figure against the sky, the tobacco glowed red against his face like a slow revolving light that is dulled by distance.

My companion was right. *Nightfall* had little more than steerage way and, though we pointed nearly up to north-west for a time, we could not hope to weather the West Mouse buoy. We watched its double white flash come a little closer to the end of our bowsprit every time the light appeared. And soon it was to windward of our course.

'Thank goodness this is only a neap tide,' I breathed. 'A three-knot spring ebb would certainly put us on the West Barrow.'

As it was the night air wafted us across the tail end of the sand in a fathom of water and brought us into the deep beyond. With the boom squared off and the falls of the mainsheet barely hanging clear of the water we trickled slowly down Swin and past the light buoy that had replaced the old pile lighthouse on the sands. Of all the seamarks in the Thames Estuary I miss the Maplin lighthouse the most, for its cheerful red colour and gaunt shape was always a welcome mark on a long passage up or down Swin, and if one were becalmed hereabouts it was interesting to anchor close by and visit the structure and yarn with the men living in the curious iron body over the spindly legs. One must go as far as Canvey to the Chapman, or away north to the Gunfleet, to see a similar pile lighthouse with its feet in the sands.

The air had begun to get that perishing chill in it that belongs to the small hours, and when I went below into the warm cabin to stoke up the fire I saw the clock said ten past one. The tide was almost at the end of its tether now and soon the flood would begin to run against us. True, it would not be a very strong flood, but two knots make all the difference when the wind is failing.

I glanced at the chart. The bright flash of the Swin Middle light float was still a mile or two ahead and there was no water over the Foulness Sands on our port beam. We could not slip across there, then, and drift up with the flood into the Crouch. Besides, we weren't bound that way. We wanted to carry on to Pin Mill in the Orwell.

'Hardly a breath now,' Dick murmured when I shut the cabin doors behind me and stood for a moment in the well, waiting for my eyes to become accustomed to the darkness.

The stillness was intense. Not a sound could be heard above the occasional creak of the gaff jaws on the mast and the musical *plop* of the drips that fell from the mainsheet on to the water. The moon, invisible above the blanket of cloud, cast a faint eerie light over the scene: it was neither moonlight nor quite pitch darkness, but a strange half glow.

'We don't seem to have shifted those lights for the past ten minutes,' Dick added in that subdued voice one instinctively uses amid the silence of open space.

'The ebb's about done,' I explained.

'I thought so.' His pipe glowed suddenly and I could see him peering towards the white pin point of light that marked the N.E. Maplin buoy. As he looked it went out. 'How about a spot of motor, eh?'

I glanced down at the engine hatch. The Morris was all ready to start up and drive us along at 6 knots, but—

'Wouldn't be much good,' I suggested. 'We could plug against the flood for a few hours and probably get into the Wallet past Clacton, but what then? D'*you* want the racket of the thing for the rest of the night?'

'Good Lord, no. But we'll start drifting back.'

'We shan't.' I dropped the lead overboard. 'Edge her in a bit closer to the sands and we'll bring up till high water. I feel quite ready to turn in.'

Within half an hour *Nightfall* lay quietly rolling with her riding light on the forestay and her anchor in the mud two fathoms below, and the young flood beginning to slip past her grey sides on its way up to London river. There was no need for an anchor watch, for no traffic was likely to come in here over the edge of the sand, and if the wind did get up suddenly I knew the changed motion would wake us better than any alarum clock.

There is something very attractive to me about these lonely anchorages away from the shore, yet protected by the sands. The fear of being caught by a sudden storm while sound asleep below, as so many yachting friends have described it in horrified terms, never worries me, for I know that the first puff, the first tremor of the yacht at some new force, would have me out in no time; and I do not anchor on what will probably be a lee shore, nor go to sleep with no reefs in and the big jib on the bowsprit, if the glass is dropping and the calm a threatening one. The skipper should use common sense, and then 'outside' anchorages need not be fraught with danger or sleepless anxiety.

By the time we awoke it was broad daylight and the breeze was springing up from the south-west. It was half-past six and the sun looked pale and watery, while I noticed that the glass had dropped a tenth since the previous night. Even as we had breakfast the dinghy came alongside and began to bump the topsides as the breeze freshened and drove the little pest over the last of the flood. And *Nightfall* began to roll and sail slowly around her anchor.

Breakfast was finished hurriedly, for the motion was rapidly becoming violent and the cups showed a tendency to join in the frolic. By a quarter-past seven we were under way with a couple of rolls in the mainboom and the working jib set, and with the freshening breeze astern of her and the ebb just about to set in her favour, *Nightfall* began a fast passage to the Swin Spitway bellbuoy. Through the spitway itself we brought the wind almost abeam and leaped wildly over the short little seas : but once in the Wallet it was a clear run to the Naze with its familiar old Trinity House tower.

The rest of the passage was like many and many others I have finished in the same waters ; squalls in Pennyhole Bay, a hurrying rush against the ebb pouring out of Harwich Harbour, more squalls at the mouth of the Stour, a sedate sail against the last hour of the ebb up the Orwell to Collimer Point, then close-hauled work as the rain began to fall up Butterman's Bay : some flirting with baffling calms and willywaws under the trees below Pin Mill, and finally almost a drift up to the anchored yachts while the rain fell from a slate grey sky and tinkled on the calm water.

' Well, it's been a variety cruise,' remarked Dick with a satisfied grin, ' and I got some nice sketches of steamers.'

With a last effort *Nightfall* rounded up to a mooring, the rusty chain grated over the fairlead, and her dripping mainsail came down with a clucking of patent sheaves as though loth to put ' Finis ' to a pleasant but undistinguished little cruise.

Still, it had been a typical Estuary one.